WHO?
WHAT?
WHEN?
WHERE?

Q. The Cisco Kid's horse was named . . . . . . ?

Q. "My little plum" is whose pet name for whom?

Q. "Is this the end of Rico?" comes from what movie?

Q. What was the destination of Hope, Crosby and Lamour in their first "Road" movie?

Q. Who was the killer in the film "This Gun for Hire"?

**JUST A FEW OF THE GREAT QUESTIONS
FROM THE FIRST GREAT BANTAM TRIVIA
QUIZ BOOK!**

THE
BANTAM
TRIVIA
QUIZ
BOOK

~~~~~~~~~~

Donald Saltz

BANTAM BOOKS · TORONTO · NEW YORK · LONDON

To my beloved wife Mozelle,
who has made my life complete.

THE BANTAM TRIVIA QUIZ BOOK
A Bantam Book / February 1975

Bantam Books are published by Bantam Books, Inc. Its trade-
mark, consisting of the words "Bantam Books" and the por-
trayal of a bantam, is registered in the United States Patent
Office and in other countries. Marca Registrada. Bantam
Books, Inc., 666 Fifth Avenue, New York, New York 10019.

PRINTED IN THE UNITED STATES OF AMERICA

Contents

Introduction

The Bantam Trivia Quiz Book is packed with thousands of facts on a variety of subjects, many of which are not found in standard history books—interesting data on movies, sports, radio and television, musicals, ad slogans, poetry, government, cars, and other topics.

The mood of America continues reflective, and that which is gone by is perhaps more in fashion than ever. A large number of high school and college students are Trivia Quiz devotees. Although most of the questions antedate their memories, they seem anxious to grasp yesteryear's popular arts—lived as youth is living its life today. It is literature, sports, advertisements, and popular arts that humanize history, and people understand this.

The old is returning more and more to the American way of life. CBS has brought back radio mystery. "The Waltons," about family life in the thirties, has a top TV rating. Stage musicals of decades ago are back, with large audiences clapping to the old refrains. Ads show replicas of old serving trays and cast-iron banks. Antique cars and furniture are valuable. Ice cream shops recapture the parlor look. Bicycling has become an important form of transportation. Firewood is in demand.

For many of us, the Trivia Quiz brings back our own "good old days"—times of study, of childhood afternoons and evenings by the radio, of movies, story telling, and riding in the family car.

The Bantam Trivia Quiz Book is a passageway to the yesteryears. Enjoy yourself there.

TELEVISION

1. Perry Como was a star singer of what radio show that moved to TV in the late 1940s?
2. "My Three Sons" began on television in 1959. Fred MacMurray was the father. Who portrayed the grandfather?
3. Who played the roles of brothers Bret and Bart Maverick?
4. Dorothy Provine was Pinky Pinkham on the show "The Roaring Twenties." She entertained at what club?
5. Name the actor who portrayed the television science instructor Mr. Wizard.
6. Irma Peterson and Jane Stacy were friends on what situation comedy television and radio show?
7. Who narrated "The Untouchables"?
8. A woman gambler by the name of Samantha Crawford appeared often on what western?
9. El Squeako Mouse, Gala Poochie, and Polka Dottie were names of puppets on what show for children which began in 1950?
10. Who was the musical director of the late-night "Broadway Open House," which featured Jerry Lester as master of ceremonies, and Dagmar?
11. "Hazel" was based on cartoons about a maid that appeared in what magazine?
12. In the earlier years of television, Lee Tracy, Lloyd Nolan, William Gargan, and Mark Stevens portrayed what detective?
13. On the television and radio show "The Goldbergs," who were the two children of Molly and Jake Goldberg?
14. Color television was first shown at the end of what decade in this century?
15. Lulu McConnell, a panel member on the radio-TV show "It Pays to Be Ignorant," was kidded most often because of what?
16. Many of the winners on "The $64,000 Question" appeared on a "sister" program. Its name?

17. Who was the creator and host of TV's "Howdy Doody" show?

18. Charles Bronson played the role of Mike Kovac, an adventurous free-lance photographer, on what show?

19. "Broadway Open House" began as a local show on NBC in New York in 1950 with who as host?

20. What was the "peanut gallery" on "Howdy Doody"?

21. In what year, within one, did "Saturday Night at the Movies" begin?

22. A television set in a clear glass cabinet was on display at the New York World's Fair in 1939. What make was it?

23. What was the original title of Phil Silvers's Sergeant Bilko show?

24. Who served as longtime host of the TV and radio show "Queen for a Day"?

25. Ben Casey was a chief resident in neurosurgery. What hospital?

26. Who was Inspector Gerard after?

27. What did Kitty Russell (Amanda Blake) often say to Matt Dillon, as an expression of warning?

28. Name the newscaster who opened with "And a good evening to you" and closed with "Glad we could get together."

29. Beulah Witch and Colonel Crackie were characters on what show for children?

30. On the radio-TV show "Life with Luigi," who was Pasquale always trying to get Luigi to marry?

31. Who played the role of Doc when "Gunsmoke" began on television?

32. Jackie Gleason's "Honeymooners" sketches were introduced on the "Cavalcade of Stars." Who portrayed his wife on the show?

33. One of the most memorable half-hour dramas on "Alcoa Theatre" was entitled "Eddie," and it was a one-person play about a desperate gambler. Who played the role?

34. What did winning contestants receive on "Feather Your Nest"?

35. One of the most humorous television presentations was an hour-long spoof of "Gunsmoke." On what show was it?

36. What was the name of the show on which Gale Gordon played the role of a high-school principal?

37. What was the "Lux Radio Theater" called when the program went to television?

38. Name the famous horror actor who played the title role in "Colonel March of Scotland Yard."

39. Name the hostess of "Blind Date."

40. Who was the regular announcer for "You Bet Your Life," featuring Groucho Marx?

41. In the mid-1950s, a husband and wife were on the panels of different shows, he on "What's My Line?" and she on "I've Got a Secret." Their names?

42. Name the prominent comedian who was opposite "Gunsmoke" in its beginning period, and who was displaced because of the high ratings of the western?

43. An auto horn was the voice of what TV show clown?

44. Television shows now called "specials" were usually called what some years ago?

45. Name the western film star who introduced the first TV episode of "Gunsmoke."

46. On what night of the week was "Gunsmoke" on TV during its earlier years?

47. What did Deputy Chester Goode call the marshal?

48. "Candid Mike" was the radio version of what later-day TV show? Who was the regular host on both radio and television?

49. Who starred as Judge Stevens and his wife in the series "I Married Joan"?

50. What character had a spaceship called the "Galaxy"?

51. Doreen Tracey, Karen Pendleton, Cubby O'Brien, Cheryl Holdridge, and Lonnie Burr were some of the members of what TV club?

52. Who had the part of Walter in the "Our Miss Brooks" series? What was Walter's last name?

53. What is the name of the dragon in "Kukla, Fran, and Ollie," and how many teeth has he?

54. Jake, Rosie, and Sammy were three of the four principal characters of what radio and television program?

55. The "Heart Fund" was a feature of what show?

56. "Challenge of the Yukon" was the theme music on what show?

57. On what radio-TV show was there a Professor Kropotkin, played by Hans Conried?

58. Who was master of ceremonies of "The $64,000 Question"?

59. What was the original name of the "Ed Sullivan Show"?

60. Alice Lon sang for six years with the Lawrence Welk orchestra before leaving in 1959. By what title was she known?

61. Virginia Ruth Egnor took the stage name of Jennie Lewis but she was well known on early television by what other name?

62. Who was master of ceremonies of "You Bet Your Life"?

63. Name the television employers of Hazel.

64. The late Eliot Ness became well known because of a book and television series about his career in Chicago. What was his occupation there?

65. "The Millionaire" was about a man whose hobby was giving away million-dollar checks to persons he believed deserving. What were the names of the millionaire and his executive secretary?

66. What did Teddy Nadler do?

Answers

1. "Chesterfield Supper Club."
2. William Frawley.
3. James Garner was Bret and Jack Kelly, Bart.
4. The Charleston Club.
5. Don Herbert.
6. "My Friend Irma."
7. Walter Winchell.
8. "Maverick."
9. "Rootie Kazootie" (also the name of a puppet).
10. Accordionist Milton Delugg.
11. "The Saturday Evening Post."
12. Martin Kane.
13. Rosalie and Sammy.
14. 1920s, by the Bell Laboratories.
15. Her heavy weight.
16. "The $64,000 Challenge."
17. Buffalo Bob Smith.
18. "Man with a Camera."
19. Morey Amsterdam.
20. The audience of children.
21. 1961, on NBC.
22. RCA.
23. "You'll Never Get Rich."
24. Jack Bailey.
25. County General Hospital.

26. Dr. Richard Kimble, the Fugitive.
27. "Be careful, Matt."
28. John Cameron Swayze.
29. "Kukla, Fran, and Ollie."
30. Pasquale's daughter Rosa.
31. Milburn Stone, then as now.
32. Pert Kelton.
33. Mickey Rooney.
34. Household furnishings.
35. The spoof was on a memorable episode of "Maverick."
36. "Our Miss Brooks." Gale Gordon was Osgood Conklin, principal of Madison High School. The show was also on radio.
37. "Lux Video Theater."
38. Boris Karloff.
39. Arlene Francis.
40. George Fenneman.
41. Steve Allen and his wife Jayne Meadows.
42. George Gobel.
43. Clarabell, on "Howdy Doody."
44. "Spectaculars."
45. John Wayne.
46. Saturday.
47. "Mr. Dillon."
48. "Candid Camera," with Allen Funt.
49. Jim Backus and Joan Davis.
50. Captain Video.
51. "The Mickey Mouse Club."
52. Richard Crenna; Denton.
53. Oliver J. Dragon; one.
54. "The Goldbergs." Molly, portrayed by Gertrude Berg, was the other.
55. "Strike It Rich."
56. "Sergeant Preston of the Yukon."
57. "My Friend Irma."
58. Hal March.
59. "Toast of the Town."
60. "Champagne Lady."
61. Dagmar.
62. Groucho Marx.
63. Stephen and Barbara Baxter.
64. Prohibition agent.
65. John Beresford Tipton was the millionaire, Michael Anthony his executive secretary.
66. He won more than a quarter-million dollars on television quiz shows during the late 1950s.

CARS

1. What was the name of the auto introduced by Pierce-Arrow in 1933 which was streamlined, had a top speed of 120 miles an hour and a cruising speed of 80, and a 12-cylinder, 175-horsepower engine?

2. What auto is mentioned in a 1905 song by Gus Edwards and Vincent P. Bryan?

3. The "Autocar" was the first U.S. motor vehicle with propulsion by shaft instead of what?

4. What manufacturer made the "Speedabout" in the late 1920s?

5. "Hitch your braggin' to this star" was in an advertisement promoting what make of auto?

6. What automobile manufacturer once owned Eastern Air Lines?

7. What auto manufacturer made the Erskine?

8. Do you know what kind of a car Freelan Stanley drove to the top of Mount Washington around the turn of the century?

9. What auto company made the Terraplane?

10. What were the Bailey, Borland, Reiker, and Wood?

11. What auto had a "Superior" model as successor to its "490" model?

12. The Coats, Victor, Wood, and Locomobile were cars that ran on what kind of power?

13. What was the Ford Motor Company's big-selling car when Henry Ford brought out the guaranteed increased wage for Ford employees?

14. What luxury car was known as the "Big D"?

15. What make of U.S. automobile has the longest history?

16. "Strength, safety, style, and speed" was a slogan used to promote what make of auto?

17. The 1939 Bantam Club roadster was built by what company?

18. What manufacturer introduced the Airflow series in 1934?

19. The first Ford Model A, which came out in 1903, had two cylinders. The Model B (1905) had four cylinders.

The Model C was brought out in 1905 too. How many cylinders did it have?

20. What auto maker had the President series, which included the Dictator and Commander lines?

21. What new, large auto manufacturer emerged in the U.S. after World War II?

22. Name the make of car with a rubber-mounted "floating power" engine.

23. What is the only surviving U.S. make of car of the dozen that were brought out half a century ago, in 1924?

24. What automobile's name was changed to Jeffery, then to Nash, and then back to its original name?

25. Hupmobiles were built from 1908 to what year, within five?

26. LaSalle, Viking, Oakland, and Marquette were part of what auto manufacturer's "family"?

27. The Packard touring car of the 1930s had a V-12 engine, wire wheels, and what kind of trunk?

28. With what auto manufacturer did Kelvinator merge?

29. Fill in the name of the car in this slogan: "Get the plus of a ———."

30. "Just a real good car" was an advertising slogan used to promote what auto?

31. The Ford Motor Company replaced its Model T with a Model A in 1927. What followed the Model A?

32. The Model A Ford, introduced in 1927, had how many cylinders?

33. "Somewhere West of Laramie" were the opening words of one of the most successful of all auto ads. It promoted what car maker?

34. After whom was the Oldsmobile named?

35. What company made a sports car called the "Bearcat" and how many persons did it seat?

36. Alex Y. Malcomson founded the Aerocar Company in 1905. Two years earlier, he had been a principal in the organization of another auto maker. That company?

37. "The car of the year in eye appeal and buy appeal" was an advertising slogan of what auto maker?

38. How many children did Henry and Clara Bryant Ford have?

39. "Ask the man who owns one" promoted what auto?

40. "Tin Lizzies" referred specifically to what autos?

41. What was the company formed in 1909 by Roy Chapin, Howard Coffin, and W. S. Hudson?

42. Jack Benny has long joked about his car. What kind is it?

43. What was the new basic wage-and-hour program for employees instituted by the Ford Motor Company in 1914?

44. In 1950, Kaiser-Frazer put out a smaller car. Name it.

45. Identify the car with the slogan "Sets the style."

46. Name the automobile advertised as being "beautiful beyond belief."

47. Name the auto company that made the Champion after World War II. The car had curved rear-deck windows, a turret top, and a bullet shape.

48. What auto manufacturer began production of the Whippet in the late 1920s?

49. What present-day car is the direct descendant of the Oakland?

50. What automobile manufacturer made the Rockne Six and Avanti?

51. The "Raceabout" was an early auto made by what company?

52. What auto manufacturers combined to form American Motors?

53. The Master Six coupe was made by what auto manufacturer?

Answers

1. "Silver Arrow."
2. Oldsmobile. (The song: "In My Merry Oldsmobile.")
3. Chain.
4. Essex.
5. Buick.
6. General Motors.
7. Studebaker.
8. Stanley Steamer.
9. Hudson.
10. Early electric autos.
11. Chevrolet.
12. Steam.
13. Model T. The new, higher wage started in 1914.
14. Duesenberg.
15. Oldsmobile, produced since 1897.
16. Hudson.
17. American Austin.

18. Chrysler.
19. Two.
20. Studebacker.
21. Kaiser-Frazer.
22. Plymouth.
23. Chrysler.
24. Rambler.
25. 1941.
26. General Motors.
27. Chest type, at the rear.
28. Nash.
29. "Packard."
30. Dodge.
31. The Ford V-8, in 1932.
32. Four.
33. Jordan, for its Playboy car.
34. Ransom Eli Olds (1864–1950), head of the Olds Motor Works around the turn of the century. The Reo auto (from his initials) was also named for him.
35. Stutz; two.
36. Ford Motor Company. His holdings equaled those of Henry Ford when the company started.
37. Studebaker.
38. One—Edsel Bryant Ford, who died in 1943 at age 49.
39. Packard.
40. Model T Fords.
41. Hudson.
42. Maxwell.
43. $5 for an eight-hour workday.
44. Henry J.
45. DeSoto.
46. Hudson.
47. Studebaker.
48. Willys-Overland.
49. Pontiac.
50. Studebaker.
51. Mercer.
52. Nash and Hudson, in 1954.
53. Chevrolet.

SHOW BUSINESS

1. Name the famous show-business daughter of Charles and Rose Borach of New York.
2. The youngest of a trio of singing sisters, Baby Frances, became one of the biggest stars in later years, known as . . . ?
3. Name the show-business personality who has joked for years about his role in the 1945 movie "The Horn Blows at Midnight."
4. What show-business personality was billed early in his career as "The World's Worst Juggler"?
5. Seven men—Georgie Jesky, Mack Riley, Charlie Avery, Edgar Kennedy, Slim Summerville, Bobby Dunn, and Hank Mann—formed a comedy team early in the century. What was the group called?
6. Who was known as the "Sweetheart of the AEF" because of her entertaining troops during World War I?
7. The "Castle Walk," "Castle Lame Duck," and "Castle House Rag" were three of the dances originated by what husband-wife dance team?
8. What entertainer would say, "You ain't heard nothin' yet, folks"?
9. What comes after "Absolutely, Mr. Gallagher"?
10. Who was the "I Don't Care Girl"?
11. Name the entertainer often billed as the "Cheerful Little Earful."
12. In 1920, an actor who called himself Ben K. Benny decided to change his name because it was too similar to that of bandleader Ben Bernie. What new name was chosen?
13. What was the occupation of Arthur Stanley Jefferson?
14. Who was known as "Ukulele Ike"?
15. Minnie Palmer was the mother of the members of what comedy team?
16. Who was the other member of the vaudeville team that included Eddie Jackson and Jimmy Durante?
17. Name the vaudeville and radio performer who was billed as "The Tune Detective."

18. Arthur Brisbane once wrote that a certain actor was "the best-known name and face in the world." To whom did he refer?

19. Mary Tomlinson Krebs has been a well-known actress for many years, but by what name?

20. Identify the character portrayed for years by Bert Gordon.

21. For what was entertainer Faith Bacon known?

22. Who was the "It" girl?

23. To whom was Carole Lombard married when she died in a plane crash in January 1942?

24. What entertainer gave the greeting, "Heigh-ho, everybody"?

25. Stage star Anna Held was married to her famous producer. His name?

26. Identify the burlesque and film star known as "The Great Stone Face."

27. Who was "The Man of a Thousand Faces"?

28. Name the comedian who created a character named "Umbriago."

29. The dance known as the "Shimmy" originated on the Barbary Coast and was introduced in New York in 1918. What was its full name?

30. Why did the popular brother-sister dancing team of Fred and Adele Astaire break up?

31. Name the trio of nightclub entertainers who worked together during the 1920s at the Dover Club, Parody Club, and Club Durante, all in New York City.

32. Four brothers formed the highest-priced act in vaudeville in 1932, getting about $10,000 a week. The act?

33. Who gained fame as a rubber-legged comedian on the stage and in movies?

34. Name the entertainer called "Bojangles."

35. Complete this old vaudeville gag: "Do short skirts make women look longer?"

36. Who says, "I'll clip ya! So help me, I'll mow ya down"?

37. W. C. Fields had a vaudeville act during which he didn't speak at all. What did he do?

38. Annually from 1915 to 1921, W. C. Fields appeared in what stage extravaganzas?

39. What adjective has long been used to describe Hildegarde?

40. Who "glorified" the American chorus girl?

41. Identify the entertainer whose real name is Hugh Krampke.

Answers

1. Fannie Brice.
2. Judy Garland. The trio was the Gumm Sisters.
3. Jack Benny.
4. Freddy James, known in later years as Fred Allen.
5. They were Mack Sennett's original "Keystone Cops."
6. Elsie Janis.
7. Vernon and Irene Castle.
8. Al Jolson, who supposedly said it for the first time as an ad lib in the film "The Jazz Singer," in 1927.
9. "Positively, Mr. Shean!" These were lines of Ed Gallagher and Al Shean.
10. Eva Tanguay.
11. Little Jack Little.
12. Jack Benny.
13. Comedian, better known as Stan Laurel.
14. Cliff Edwards.
15. The Marx Brothers.
16. Lou Clayton.
17. Sigmund Spaeth.
18. Francis X. Bushman.
19. Marjorie Main.
20. "Mad Russian."
21. She was a fan and bubble dancer before Sally Rand. Miss Bacon appeared in an ostrich fan costume in the "Earl Carroll Vanities of 1930," in New York.
22. Clara Bow.
23. Clark Gable.
24. Rudy Vallee.
25. Florenz Ziegfeld.
26. Buster Keaton.
27. Lon Chaney.
28. Jimmy Durante.
29. "Shimmy Shewabble."
30. Adele Astaire married in 1934, dissolving the act.
31. Lou Clayton, Eddie Jackson and Jimmy Durante.
32. The Marx Brothers.
33. Leon Errol.
34. Bill Robinson.
35. "No, but they make men look longer."
36. Edgar Bergen's dummy, Charlie McCarthy.
37. He was a juggler.
38. Ziegfeld Follies.
39. "Incomparable."
40. Florenz Ziegfeld.
41. Hugh O'Brian.

PRESIDENTS

1. During his second administration, President Franklin D. Roosevelt attempted to win the right to add how many justices to the U.S. Supreme Court?
2. What Congress did President Truman denounce during the 1948 presidential election campaign?
3. Name the Democrat who received more popular votes than his Republican opponent in the 1876 presidential election, but lost.
4. Who was the Republican candidate for President when the party's nominee for Vice-President was Sen. Charles L. McNary of Oregon?
5. Ruth, Esther, Marion, Richard, and Francis were children of what President?
6. What U.S. President was nicknamed "Old Rough and Ready"?
7. What were President Franklin D. Roosevelt's speeches to the nation generally called?
8. What was the symbol of Theodore Roosevelt's Progressive party?
9. Name the first President born in a log cabin.
10. What was the breed of Franklin Roosevelt's dog Fala?
11. Two U.S. Presidents each served less than a year in office. Name at least one of them.
12. What President-to-be in 1928 called Prohibition "A great social and economic experiment noble in motive and far-reaching in purpose"?
13. Andrew Johnson was the second U.S. Vice-President to serve with President Abraham Lincoln. Who was the first?
14. Name at least two of the four sons of Abraham and Mary Lincoln.
15. The slogan "Tippecanoe and Tyler, too" was used in the successful campaign of what candidate for President?
16. After the 1936 presidential election, the old political adage "As Maine goes, so goes the nation" was changed to what?
17. President Franklin D. Roosevelt, a Democrat, named

what staunch Republican as Secretary of the Navy, a
cabinet post, in 1940?

18. Elizabeth Virginia Wallace was the maiden name of
what former first lady?

19. How many children did George and Martha Washington have?

20. Name the U.S. President whose children were named
Robert, Helen, and Charles.

21. Two Presidents were survived by their fathers. One was
President Kennedy. The other?

22. Who was the second President to serve only one term in
office?

23. Name the first President to receive an annual salary of
$100,000.

24. Schuyler Colfax and Henry Wilson were Vice-Presidents
under what President?

25. Who was mistress of the White House during the administration of bachelor President James Buchanan?

26. Name the President-to-be whose wife and mother died
on the same day.

27. John Tyler had the most children of any U.S. President. Within three, how many?

28. What relation was Theodore Roosevelt to Mrs. Franklin
D. (Eleanor) Roosevelt?

29. What in particular made President Buchanan different
from all other U.S. Presidents, before and since?

30. Which one of Abraham Lincoln's sons served in a President's Cabinet? What post did he hold?

31. The 24th Democratic party convention, in New York in
1924, was the longest nominating convention of a major
political party. John W. Davis was finally chosen as the
presidential nominee on what ballot?

32. The phrase "smoke-filled room" was first used at a Republican party convention in Chicago. By whom?

33. What was Steve Early's position in President Franklin
D. Roosevelt's administration?

34. Which incumbent did John F. Kennedy defeat when he
first ran for the U.S. Senate in 1952?

35. Wendell L. Willkie was president of a large corporation
prior to his nomination as the Republican party's candidate for President in 1940. Its name?

36. Who was the other U.S. Senator from Texas when Lyn-
don Johnson was elected to the Senate in 1948?

37. Where was Calvin Coolidge sworn in as President after the death of President Harding?

38. "I am as strong as a bull moose," Theodore Roosevelt observed in 1900. To whom did he make this statement?

39. Only two of the then 48 states were carried by Republican presidential candidate Alfred M. Landon in 1936. Name them.

40. Who was the vice-presidential nominee on the States' Rights ticket in 1948?

41. Who operated the boardinghouse into which President Lincoln was carried after he was shot?

42. Calvin Coolidge said, "There is no right to strike against the public safety by anybody, anywhere, anytime." To whom did he make this statement?

43. Franklin D. Roosevelt never carried his home county in four successful presidential campaigns. What was his home county?

44. To which member of the Roosevelt family was Faye Emerson married?

45. Name the first U.S. President of the Quaker faith.

46. Of what college was President Coolidge a graduate?

47. To what political office was Andrew Johnson elected after he had served as President?

48. "We here highly resolve that these dead shall not have died in vain" was said by whom on what occasion?

49. Name the President who said before one of his party's national conventions that "older men declare war, but it is youth that must fight and die . . ."

50. Who was the Secretary of the Interior involved in the Teapot Dome scandal during the Harding administration?

51. What President-to-be did Helen Herron marry?

52. Mary Ball was the maiden name of the mother of what President?

53. What relation if any, were Presidents William Henry Harrison and Benjamin Harrison?

54. Eleanor Roosevelt was editor of what Macfadden publication when her husband was elected President for the first time, in 1932?

55. Spell the nickname by which President James Madison's wife—Dorothea Dandridge Payne Todd Madison—was known.

56. How old was Theodore Roosevelt when he became President? He was the youngest man to hold the office.

57. James Buchanan was the only President who never married, but another bachelor was elected to that office. He later married. Can you identify him?

58. What statement by President Franklin D. Roosevelt preceded these words in his first inaugural address—"nameless, unreasoning, unjustified terror which paralyzes needed efforts to convert retreat into advance"?

59. In what two cities was George Washington inaugurated President?

60. What did John Wilkes Booth shout after he shot President Lincoln?

61. Seven of the 12 Presidents from Ulysses S. Grant through Warren G. Harding were from which state?

62. When King George VI and Queen Elizabeth of England joined President and Mrs. Roosevelt for a picnic at Hyde Park, N.Y., on a day in June 1939, what was the principal food item served?

63. What candidate for President campaigned from jail during the 1920 preelection period? He received 920,000 votes.

64. Of what university was Woodrow Wilson president?

65. How many electoral votes were in dispute in the presidential election of 1876, between Rutherford B. Hayes, Republican, and Samuel J. Tilden, Democrat? What happened to the disputed votes?

66. Name the first Republican nominee for President.

67. Who were the two Democratic nominees for Vice-President in the 1950s?

68. Who was the only man to serve as both President and Chief Justice of the U.S.?

Answers

1. Six, for a total of 15.
2. The Republican-controlled 80th.
3. Samuel J. Tilden.
4. Wendell L. Willkie.
5. Grover Cleveland.
6. Zachary Taylor.
7. Fireside chats.
8. A bull moose.
9. Andrew Jackson, seventh President.

10. Scotch terrier.
11. William Henry Harrison (32 days) and James A. Garfield (199 days).
12. Herbert Hoover.
13. Hannibal Hamlin.
14. Robert, Edward, William, and Thomas (Tad).
15. William Henry Harrison (1840).
16. "As Maine goes, so goes Vermont." Only Maine and Vermont went for the Republican candidate for President that year, Kansas Governor Alfred M. Landon.
17. Frank Knox.
18. Mrs. Harry Truman.
19. None. Martha had four children by her previous husband, Daniel Parke Custis.
20. William Howard Taft.
21. Warren G. Harding.
22. John Quincy Adams, the sixth President. The first President to serve only one term was John Adams, the second President of the U.S. John Quincy Adams was the son of John Adams.
23. President Truman, in 1949. It had been $75,000.
24. Ulysses S. Grant.
25. His niece, Harriet Lane. Her parents had died when she was very young.
26. Theodore Roosevelt. His mother and first wife, Alice, both died on February 14, 1884.
27. Tyler had 15 children, eight by one wife and seven by another.
28. Uncle.
29. He never married.
30. Robert T. Lincoln was Secretary of War under Presidents Garfield and Arthur 1881–85).
31. 103d.
32. Harry M. Daugherty, Warren G. Harding's manager.
33. Presidential press secretary.
34. Henry Cabot Lodge.
35. Commonwealth and Southern Electric Utilities Company.
36. Tom Connally.
37. The Coolidge family homestead, Plymouth, Vt.
38. Mark Hanna, in a letter.
39. Maine and Vermont.
40. Govenor Fielding L. Wright of Mississippi.
41. William Peterson.
42. Samuel Gompers, president of the American Federation of Labor, in a telegram (1919). Coolidge was referring to a strike by Boston policemen. Coolidge was Governor of Massachusetts at the time.
43. Dutchess, in New York State.
44. President Franklin D. Roosevelt's son Elliott.
45. Herbert Hoover.
46. Amherst.
47. He was elected to the U.S. Senate from Tennessee.
48. President Abraham Lincoln, Gettysburg, Pa., Nov. 19, 1863. The excerpt is from Lincoln's Gettysburg Address, delivered at the dedica-

tion of a military cemetery. A terrible battle had been fought between forces of the North and South in early July.

49. Herbert Hoover.
50. Albert B. Fall.
51. William Howard Taft.
52. George Washington.
53. William Henry was Benjamin's grandfather.
54. "Babies."
55. Dolley.
56. He was 42, less than two months shy of his 43d birthday.
57. Grover Cleveland.
58. ". . . the only thing we have to fear is fear itself . . ."
59. New York (1789) and Philadelphia (1793).
60. "Sic semper tyrannis" ("Ever thus to tyrants").
61. Ohio, home state of Presidents Grant, Hayes, Garfield, Benjamin Har-
    rison, McKinley, Taft, and Harding.
62. Hot dogs (served with cold beer).
63. Socialist Eugene Debs.
64. Princeton.
65. A total of 20 were disputed, 19 from three southern states and 1
    from Oregon. All 20 went to Hayes, as determined by a special com-
    mission, and he won the election by 185–184.
66. John C. Fremont (1856).
67. Senators John J. Sparkman of Alabama and Estes Kefauver of Ten-
    nessee, in 1952 and '56 respectively.
68. William Howard Taft.

CRIME

1. Name the woman who operated "crime schools" in the Kansas City, Toledo, and Ocala, Fla., areas, and who was killed in 1935 while shooting at FBI agents with a machine gun.
2. Bruno Richard Hauptmann was convicted for kidnapping the Lindbergh baby in 1932, and was sentenced to death. Where was the trial held?
3. In 1949, a federal grand jury convicted Mildred Elizabeth Gillars of a crime and she was sentenced to a prison term of 10 to 30 years. What crime did she commit?
4. What newspaper originated the name "Murder, Incorporated"?
5. Charles Mattson, William A. Hamm, Jr., and Robert C. Greenlease were all victims of what crime?
6. In March 1949, Judith Coplon was arrested in New York. What was the charge placed against her?
7. Who was chairman of the Senate Committee to Investigate Organized Crime in Interstate Commerce when that committee exposed nationwide criminal organizations in 1951?
8. Who first applied the title "G-men" to agents of the FBI?
9. Name the man who became nationally known after escaping from a Georgia chain gang. He wrote the book "I Am a Fugitive from a Chain Gang," later made into a movie.
10. Who shot and killed outlaw Jesse James?
11. Name the attorney whose dramatic plea was credited with saving the lives of murderers Richard Loeb and Nathan Leopold.
12. Do you know the first name of Jesse James's wife?
13. William H. Bonney, a native of New York City, became a criminal. How did he break the law?
14. Name the chief defense counsel in the famous Scopes trial.

15. Lester Gillis was a notorious criminal, known by what name?

16. The federal government had Al Capone tried for what crime? He was convicted and sentenced to prison for 11 years.

17. Of what criminal gang were Homer Van Meter, John Paul Chase, and John Hamilton members?

18. In what city did police capture John Dillinger, Charles Makley, Russell Clark, and Harry Pierpont in January 1934?

19. In June 1934, how much reward did the government offer for the capture of John Dillinger dead or alive?

20. Arthur Flegenheimer, an underworld principal of the 1930s, was better known by what name?

Answers

1. Kate (Ma) Barker.
2. Flemington, N.J.
3. Treason, for broadcasting Nazi propaganda during World War II. She was known as "Axis Sally."
4. New York World-Telegram.
5. Kidnapping.
6. Espionage on behalf of Russia.
7. Senator Estes Kefauver.
8. George (Machine Gun) Kelly, who when caught in 1933 begged, "Don't shoot, G-men! Don't shoot, G-men!"
9. Robert Elliott Burns.
10. Bob Ford, a member of the James gang.
11. Clarence Darrow.
12. Zeralda, or Zee.
13. He was a cattle thief and killer, better known as "Billy the Kid."
14. Clarence Darrow.
15. "Baby Face Nelson."
16. Income-tax evasion.
17. The Dillinger gang.
18. Tucson, Ariz.
19. $10,000 for his capture, and $5,000 for information leading to his arrest.
20. "Dutch Schultz."

COMICS

1. Name the creator of the cartoon character Judge Puffle.
2. Mickey Finn was an athlete in the early days of the "Mickey Finn" comic strip. In what sport did he participate?
3. What was the title of the tramp strip started by C. D. Russell in 1932?
4. Otto Soglow's "The Little King" was transferred to "Puck, the Comic Weekly" in 1934. Name the publication in which it had appeared.
5. In the comics, who was Toro, the Flaming Kid?
6. Who was the stretchy hero of Police Comics?
7. What was the usual number of pages contained in 10-cent comic books of the late 1930s and 1940s?
8. Walt Wallet, a character in "Gasoline Alley," is the father of Skeezix, Corky, and Judy. Whom did Walt marry?
9. In what century is spaceman Buck Rogers supposed to be living?
10. What do comic strip characters "Henry" and "The Little King" have in common?
11. "Steamboat Willie" was the first movie starring what popular cartoon character?
12. Andy, Min, Chester, and Uncle Bim were featured in what strip?
13. "Thimble Theatre, Starring Popeye" features a character named Wimpy whose delight is eating hamburgers. Name the man who runs the restaurant where Wimpy eats most of his hamburgers.
14. In what branch of military service did Joe Palooka serve during World War II?
15. Lai Choi San (meaning "Mountain of Wealth") was a character who made an appearance in the early days of "Terry and the Pirates." By what name did she become better known?
16. Name the father of Little Iodine.
17. What is the first name of the wife of Snuffy Smith?

18. Back in the 1930s, Jerry Siegel and Joe Shuster combined their efforts to turn out what strip?

19. In what strip was Ignatz Mouse to be found?

20. What was the original name of the "Mary Worth" strip?

21. In 1947, Milton Caniff gave up the strip he was drawing and began a new one. Name the two.

22. The Shmoo has appeared periodically in what comic strip?

23. What was the original title of the "Mutt and Jeff" strip?

24. In what strip was there once a villain named Pruneface?

25. How old is Skeezix in "Gasoline Alley"?

26. What is the best-known song in which a character from the comics is mentioned?

27. By what name was cartoonist T. A. Dorgan known?

28. Business tycoon J. P. McKee has appeared in what strip?

29. Name the popular animal strip that was drawn by George Herriman.

30. Do you know the full first name of Steve Canyon?

31. What famous early strip, begun in newspapers in the 1890s, was drawn by Richard Outcault and later by George Luks?

32. A comic-strip artist once offered a prize for the "most gruesome" face for his character Lena the Hyena, and a million persons responded. Name the strip and the artist.

33. Name Little Annie Rooney's dog.

34. The comic strip "Show-Girl" evolved into one with what title?

35. Who was Abie Kabibble?

36. Name the newsboy who became a comic-book hero.

37. Jay Garrick inhaled gas fumes in a laboratory experiment and soon became what comic-book hero?

38. Ham Gravy and Cole Oyl are two of the characters who appeared in what comic strip?

39. What was the original name of Mickey Mouse?

40. If Little Orphan Annie aged a year for every year she was in the comic strip, how much older would she be—within five years—in 1975?

41. Tagalong was a character in what strip?

42. Name the flying, caped hero seen regularly in Whiz Comics.

43. "J. Wellington" is the first initial and middle name of what comic-strip character?

44. What is the occupation of the Inspector in "The Katzenjammer Kids"?

45. What comic-strip hero, according to the story line, is from Wilkes-Barre, Pa.?

46. Aunt Eppie Hogg and Terrible Tempered Mr. Bang were two characters in a popular strip by Fontaine Fox. Its title?

47. What was the name of Captain America's young sidekick?

48. What kind of a mammal was Ignatz in "Krazy Kat"?

49. Otto Soglow created "Sentinel Louie," but what is the name of his best known comic strip?

50. What was the name of Dinglehoofer's dog?

51. Dr. Sivana was a villain who opposed what hero of the comic books?

52. "Rosie's Beau" was by George McManus, who was better known for another strip—name it.

53. Who were the comic-strip owners of the dog Spare-Ribs?

54. In an old-time strip, what kind of animal was Maud?

55. Complete the name of this strip: "Boots and Her———."

56. Name the creator of "Toonerville Folks."

57. Clark Kent and Superman live in what mythical city?

58. In 1943, Roy Crane relinquished "Wash Tubbs" to start a new strip. Do you know its name?

59. "Notary Sojac" is a term that appears in what strip?

60. What was considered the first outright family comic strip?

61. The word "Jeep" was introduced in what strip?

62. Name the creator of both "Mandrake the Magician" and "The Phantom."

63. The Cat Woman, the Riddler, Two-Face, and Dr. Death were villains who fought what hero?

64. What comic-book hero is from the mythical planet Krypton?

65. The concocted word "bodacious" has long appeared in what strip?

66. Comic-book character Prince Namor was known by what other name?

67. What was the occupation of Superman's father?

68. In what comic book did the "Green Lantern" appear regularly?

69. Name the daughter of Dick Tracy and Tess Trueheart Tracy.

70. "The Man of Steel" is also called "The Man of Tomorrow." Who is he?

71. What was the name of the dog with Uncle Elby?

72. What was the name of the policeman in the "Krazy Kat" strip?

73. Wilma Deering was a character in what strip?

74. Who drew the panel "Thrill That Comes Once in a Lifetime"?

75. Colonel Hoofer was a character in what husband-wife strip?

76. In the "Smilin' Jack" strip, who was Cherry's mother?

77. The spoken word "SHAZAM" turned Billy Batson into Captain Marvel. For what did the "S" of that magic word stand?

78. Name the cat in the "Smokey Stover" comic strip.

79. In what strip were there Rocket Rangers for boys and girls?

80. Fill in the missing word in the title of the comic strip "Dinglehoofer———His Dog."

81. Who was the girl friend of Ibis the magician?

82. A vat of acid spilled on a crook named Eel O'Brian, eventually turning him into what superhero?

83. Who was Queen of the Jungle and in what comic book was she a regular feature?

84. Who was Madge Milquetoast?

85. What was the name of the comic strip with characters Ma and Pa Cinders and Blackie?

86. Woozy Winks was whose sidekick?

87. Where was the home of Prince Namor?

88. Dinty Moore was a character in what long-run comic strip?

89. Name Little Lulu's regular boyfriend.

90. What was the occupation of Hawkshaw?

91. A woman drew the strip "Cap Stubbs and Tippie." Can you identify her?

Answers

1. Eugene Ahern.
2. Wrestling.
3. "Pete the Tramp."
4. "New Yorker" magazine.
5. He was the sidekick of the Human Torch.
6. Plastic Man.
7. 64.
8. Phyllis Blos
9. 25th centur
10. Neither of t   speak.
11. Walt Disney'   Mouse.
12. "The Gumps."
13. Rough-House.
14. Army.
15. "The Dragon Lady."
16. Henry Tremblechin.
17. Loweezy.
18. "Superman."
19. "Krazy Kat."
20. "Apple Mary" (created by Martha Orr).
21. Caniff relinquished "Terry and the Pirates" and started drawing "Steve Canyon."
22. "Li'l Abner."
23. "A. Mutt," started by Bud Fisher in 1907.
24. "Dick Tracy."
25. He was born in 1921, so in 1975 he is 54 years old. Characters in this strip "age."
26. "Barney Google" (with the goo-goo-googly eyes).
27. "TAD."
28. "Captain Easy."
29. "Krazy Kat."
30. Stevenson.
31. "Yellow Kid."
32. "Li'l Abner"; Al Capp.
33. Zero.
34. "Dixie Dugan."
35. The main character in the old comic strip "Abie the Agent."
36. Billy Batson, who became Captain Marvel.
37. The Flash.
38. "Thimble Theatre, Starring Popeye."
39. Mortimer Mouse.
40. The comic strip was created by Harold Gray in 1924. Annie would be 51 plus her original age in the strip.
41. "Freckles and His Friends."
42. Captain Marvel.
43. Wimpy, in Popeye strips.
44. Truant officer.
45. Joe Palooka.

46. "Toonerville Folks."
47. Bucky Barnes.
48. Ignatz was a mouse.
49. "The Little King."
50. Schnappsy.
51. Captain Marvel.
52. "Bringing Up Father" (with Maggie and Jiggs).
53. Toots and Casper.
54. A mule.
55. "Buddies."
56. Fontaine Fox.
57. Metropolis.
58. "Buz Sawyer."
59. "Smokey Stover."
60. "The Gumps," which began in 1917.
61. "Thimble Theatre, Starring Popeye," in 1932.
62. Lee Falk.
63. Batman.
64. Superman.
65. "Snuffy Smith."
66. Submariner.
67. He was a scientist who put his infant son (later to become Superman) in an experimental rocket ship and launched it toward Earth before Krypton exploded into fragments.
68. "All-American Comics."
69. Bonny Braids.
70. Superman.
71. Napoleon.
72. Offissa B. Pupp.
73. "Buck Rogers in the 25th Century."
74. Harold T. Webster.
75. "Toots and Casper."
76. Cindy.
77. Solomon's wisdom.
78. Spooky.
79. "Buck Rogers in the 25th Century."
80. ". . . und . . ."
81. Taia.
82. Plastic Man.
83. Sheena was the Queen of the Jungle and she appeared in "Jumbo Comics."
84. The wife of Casper Milquetoast, the "Timid Soul." The comic strip was by H.T. Webster.
85. "Ella Cinders."
86. Plastic Man's.
87. The lost continent of Atlantis. (He was the Submariner.)
88. "Bringing Up Father" (with Maggie and Jiggs).
89. Tubby.
90. Detective.
91. Edwina Dumm.

MILITARY

1. General Robert E. Lee commanded Confederate forces during the battles at Gettysburg, Pa., in July 1863. Who was in charge of the Union forces there?

2. The Atlantic Charter was signed by President Roosevelt and Prime Minister Churchill aboard what ship?

3. What was the native state of World War I hero Alvin York? During which offensive by the Allies did he kill at least 25 enemy soldiers and capture 132 prisoners?

4. Name at least two of the four statesmen—leaders of the Big Four Nations—who participated in the Treaty of Versailles.

5. On several occasions prior to the Pearl Harbor attack, the U.S. ambassador to Japan warned of possible sudden war started by Japan. Name him.

6. U.S. Marines fought in Peking, China, in 1900 in a campaign referred to as the ———— ————.

7. Perhaps the most famous picture of World War II is the one of Americans raising a flag during a battle on Iwo Jima. The photo won a Pulitzer prize and was used on posters for War Bond drives. What is the name of the mountain on which the flag was hoisted?

8. Japan seized control of Manchuria in 1932 and renamed it. What was the new name?

9. What was the full rank of General John J. Pershing?

10. What important roles did Kurusu and Nomura have in December 1941?

11. The Duke of Wellington and Count von Blücher clashed with Napoleon at Waterloo. In what country?

12. With what nation did Germany sign a nonaggression treaty on August 24, 1939?

13. Name two of the three countries that were part of the Triple Alliance formed in 1717 against Spain.

14. What foreign power was responsible for the sinking of the U.S. gunboat "Panay" in 1937?

15. The Spanish-American War was touched off in 1898 by the blowing up of the U.S. battleship "Maine." Where did this occur?

16. Who led the U.S. military force that unsuccessfully

sought Mexican revolutionary leader Pancho Villa in 1916–17?

17. What major event in U.S. history occurred on April 6, 1917?

18. What kind of bomber was used in James Doolittle's raid on Japan in April 1942, only a few months after the U.S. entered World War II?

19. Name the American commander of the frigate "Chesapeake" who said, "Don't give up the ship," during the War of 1812.

20. In what year of World War II did about 300,000 British and French soldiers manage to escape from Dunkirk?

21. During the Civil War, the Confederates renamed the ironclad "Merrimac" what?

22. The Semper Paratus Always Ready Service has been a women's branch of what?

23. Germany was allowed to take over part of Czechoslovakia in 1938, but World War II began in 1939 when Germany went to war with what country?

24. The so-called "Lost Battalion" during World War I finally emerged from what noted battle?

25. What was General Douglas MacArthur's primary job after World War II ended?

26. Union and Confederate forces fought desperately for control of Little Round Top Hill during the Civil War. Its location?

27. The costly battle of the Meuse-Argonne occurred in what year?

28. The First U.S. Volunteer Cavalry, recruited by Lieutenant Colonel Theodore Roosevelt, fought in the Spanish-American War. By what name was the volunteer group known?

29. General Douglas MacArthur promised to return when he was leaving what island for Australia, in March 1942?

30. In early 1942, Lieutenant Colonel James Doolittle led 16 B-25s from an aircraft carrier for a surprise attack on Japanese cities. The planes took off from what carrier?

31. What Union Army general told President Lincoln, in late 1864: "I beg to present you as a Christmas gift the city of Savannah"?

32. In June 1942, Dwight D. Eisenhower was appointed commander of U.S. forces in the European theater of war. What was his rank at the time?

33. What city was taken from the British and occupied by George Washington and his troops during the Christmas 1776 period?

34. In 1934, three military men ascended over 11 miles. In what?

Answers

1. Major General George G. Meade.
2. The British battleship "Prince of Wales" (1941).
3. Tennessee; Meuse-Argonne offensive.
4. Premier Vittorio Orlando of Italy; Prime Minister Lloyd George of England; Premier Georges Clemenceau of France; President Woodrow Wilson of the U.S.
5. Joseph C. Grew.
6. Boxer Rebellion.
7. Mount Suribachi.
8. Manchukuo.
9. General of the Armies.
10. They were Japanese envoys engaged in talks with U.S. Secretary of State Cordell Hull when their country's military forces attacked Pearl Harbor.
11. Belgium.
12. Soviet Union.
13. England, Holland, France.
14. Japan.
15. Harbor of Havana, Cuba.
16. General John J. Pershing.
17. The U.S. declared war on Germany, entering World War I.
18. The B-25.
19. James Lawrence.
20. 1940.
21. "Virginia."
22. Coast Guard (SPARS).
23. Poland.
24. Meuse-Argonne.
25. Military governor of Japan.
26. Gettysburg, Pa.
27. 1918, final year of World War I.
28. Rough Riders.
29. Corregidor, in the Philippines.
30. "Hornet."
31. William Tecumseh Sherman.
32. Major general.
33. Trenton, N.J.
34. A balloon.

MOVIES

1. Clark Gable was married five times. Name at least two of his wives.
2. If Humphrey Bogart were living, how old would he be in 1975?
3. Complete these Joan Crawford movie titles: "Female on the————," "The Shining————," and "Torch————."
4. Actor Raymond Griffith played the role of a dying French soldier in a famous film, released in 1930. What is its title?
5. Who said, "Monkeys iss duh cwaziest people"?
6. Three actresses portray sisters in "Three Smart Girls." Identify at least one of the actresses.
7. Who are the stars of the 1943 20th Century-Fox comedy "Jitterbugs"?
8. Shirley Temple plays Dimples in the 1936 movie of that name. Who portrays her guardian?
9. Actor John Gilbert had what color hair and eyes?
10. Clark Gable was called the————of Hollywood. Fill in the blank.
11. Name the actress who starred in "Daughter of the Dragon," "Shanghai Express," and "Dangerous to Know."
12. The MGM movie "The Champ" tells the story of an old prizefighter and his young son. Name the actors who play the two roles.
13. Gregory Peck, Harry Shannon, Richard Jaeckel, Karl Malden, and Jean Parker star in a 1950 western considered one of the best films of all time. Its title?
14. Helen Chandler and Dwight Frye appeared with Bela Lugosi in what famous horror picture, released in 1931?
15. Who performed the famous "human fly" stunt in the silent "Safety Last"?
16. What weird character was played in the movies by Lon Chaney, Sr., in the 1920s, Claude Rains in the 1940s, and Herbert Lom in the 1960s?
17. Who portrays German Field Marshal Rommel in the 1943 movie "Five Graves to Cairo"?

18. What longtime star, whose career began in 1925, was actually named Billie Cassin and was known on the stage as Lucille LeSueur?

19. Identify the picture, starring Charles Boyer, in which the catchphrase "Come with me to the Casbah" was introduced.

20. James Dean made his debut in "East of Eden," released by Warner Brothers in 1955. His final picture was released by Warner in 1956. What is its title?

21. The 1940 Warner Brothers release "Castle on the Hudson," starring Pat O'Brien, Ann Sheridan, and John Garfield, depicts life where?

22. Name one of the two actresses who starred as the singing and dancing Dolly Sisters in the 1945 movie of that title.

23. One of Humphrey Bogart's finest roles is believed to be the one in "The Maltese Falcon," a detective story released by Warner Brothers in 1941. What is his role?

24. In order to get Clark Gable for the role of Rhett Butler in "Gone with the Wind," producer David O. Selznick agreed to release the picture through Gable's studio. Which was Gable's studio?

25. Irvin S. Cobb appears with what child actress in "Pepper" (1936)?

26. John Gilbert and Mae Murray starred in a 1925 movie which was remade, utilizing sound, in 1934 with Maurice Chevalier and Jeanette MacDonald as the stars. The title?

27. In what picture does Mae West say to Gilbert Roland, "I collect diamonds . . . it's m' hobby"?

28. Carole Lombard's last movie was "To Be or Not to Be," released by United Artists in 1942. With whom did she costar?

29. In "The Gold Rush," Charlie Chaplin portrays a starving prospector who attempts to eat something completely out of the food line. What?

30. During World War I, Humphrey Bogart served in the U.S. Navy. His ship was shelled and this caused what to happen to him physically?

31. What actress may be seen holding children in the pictures "Common Clay" (1930), "Born to Love" (1931), and "Rockabye" (1932)?

32. In "The Public Enemy," James Cagney pushes half a grapefruit into the face of what actress?

33. What is the "Thing" in the 1951 movie of that title?

34. What is the title of the 1936 Fox film starring Shirley Temple, Guy Kibbee, Buddy Ebsen, and Slim Summerville, among others?

35. What actor and actress romanced together for the first time on the screen in the 1927 picture "Flesh and the Devil"?

36. Who portrayed a legless man in "The Penalty" (1920), a one-eyed man in "The Road to Mandalay" (1926), and a paralytic in "West of Zanzibar" (1929)?

37. Identify the cowboy film star who was a sheriff of counties in Kansas and Oklahoma, a deputy U.S. marshal, and a Texas ranger.

38. Evelyn Venable, Louis Dresser, Kent Taylor, and Stepin Fetchit are featured in the 1934 picture "David Harum." Who has the title role?

39. Lionel Barrymore, Lewis Stone, Edward Arnold, and Grant Mitchell costar in what MGM release of the mid-1940s, about a girl who believes in leprechauns?

40. Lon Chaney played in many films but in only one talkie. Which one?

41. In what movie does Charlie Chaplin appear to be a large chicken to a hunger-crazed companion?

42. What western hero had a horse named Pinto Ben?

43. In the classic "Grand Hotel," Joan Crawford is Flämmchen, a young woman whose occupation is what?

44. The 1931 "Cimarron" features Irene Dunne, William Collier, Jr., and an actor who appears in what is considered his finest role. His name?

45. An actor whose real name was Max Aronson and who used the stage name of Gilbert M. Anderson was known by still another name after he became the first western star. What was it?

46. What role in "Boys Town" did a boy named Bobs Watson play?

47. In which of W. C. Fields's movies does he dive from an airplane after a fallen bottle of whiskey and land on a mountaintop where he meets a girl who has never seen a man before?

48. "Der Führer's Face" won an Academy Award as the

best cartoon of 1942. It featured what Walt Disney character?

49. Who portrays Uncle Charlie, murderer of rich widows, in Alfred Hitchcock's "Shadow of a Doubt"?

50. May McAvoy, John Gilbert, Greta Garbo, and Gloria Swanson were all acting in movies when the silent era gave way to sound. The voices of two were considered unsatisfactory for sound films. Which two?

51. What kind of role was usually played by Maxie Rosenbloom?

52. In "The Man on the Flying Trapeze," Ambrose Wolfinger (W. C. Fields) goes to the basement of his house to check on burglars. All of them end up drinking applejack and singing what song?

53. Who plays the part of the scientist creator of apemen in the 1932 "Island of Lost Souls"?

54. Dooley Wilson sings "As Time Goes By" in "Casablanca." What other song does he sing in the film?

55. What do Scotty Mattraw, Roy Atwell, Pinto Colvig, Otis Harlan, and Billy Gilbert do in "Snow White and the Seven Dwarfs"?

56. What is W. C. Fields's role in the 1935 movie "David Copperfield"?

57. Name the creator of slapstick comedy who joined the Biograph studio in 1911 and within a couple of years headed the Keystone Company.

58. The song "Who's Afraid of the Big, Bad Wolf?" was popularized in what Disney cartoon short?

59. In "My Little Chickadee," starring W. C. Fields and Mae West, Fields is mistaken for a bandit and is about to be hanged. He is asked if he has any last request and replies, "Yes, I'd like to see Paris before I die." As the noose tightens, what words does he add?

60. Name the little boy actor who was W. C. Fields's nemesis.

61. In what picture does Clark Gable say, "Take a good look at them so you can tell your grandchildren that you saw the rear guard of the Glorious Cause in retreat"?

62. Who are the top two male stars who appear with Humphrey Bogart in the 1938 "Angels with Dirty Faces"? This film marks an early screen appearance of the Dead End Kids.

63. Name the studio that inaugurated the "Our Gang" series.

64. The first song to win an Academy Award was "The Continental," which is in what Fred Astaire—Ginger Rogers musical of 1934?

65. Cary Grant said to Mae West, "Surely you don't mind my holding your hand?" What did she reply? (The picture is "She Done Him Wrong.")

66. Can you name the male star who debuted in "The Painted Desert" and appeared in many other pictures, including "Test Pilot," "Boom Town," and "The King and Four Queens"?

67. What is the relationship between actress Shirley MacLaine and actor Warren Beatty?

68. Who performs the dance routine "Bojangles of Harlem" in the mid-1930s "Swing Time"?

69. What kind of animal is "Thumper" and in what Disney movie does he appear?

70. The song "Over the Rainbow" was first heard in what movie of the late 1930s? Who sang it?

71. Who was the first actor to play Tarzan on the screen?

72. In what film does Bogart say, "Nobody gets the best of Fred C. Dobbs"?

73. Who blows the head off an ice-cream soda in "Never Give a Sucker an Even Break"?

74. Who portrays Captain Bligh in the 1935 "Mutiny on the Bounty"? Who portrays the captain in the 1962 version?

75. Who sings "Rose in Her Hair" and "Lulu's Back in Town" in "Broadway Gondolier"?

76. Winner of an Academy Award for best picture of the year in 1959 was "Ben-Hur." Who won the best actor award for his role in the movie?

77. Name either the actor who plays the bachelor or the actress who portrays the bobby-soxer in "The Bachelor and the Bobby-Soxer."

78. For her portrayal in what picture did Joan Crawford win an Academy Award as best actress?

79. Who portrays the killer in the early 1940s film "This Gun for Hire"?

80. What is the destination of Bob Hope, Bing Crosby, and Dorothy Lamour in their first "Road" movie?

81. Name the character in "Pinocchio" who is seen singing

"When You Wish upon a Star" over the film's main title, and then on a shelf above a Pinocchio storybook.

82. What is the substance that Professor Ned Brainard (Fred MacMurray) accidentally invents in "The Absent Minded Professor"? The film was released by Buena Vista in 1961.

83. Charlie Chase was one of Mack Sennett's Keystone Cops back in 1912. Later he was a director for the Sennett and other studios. He returned to the screen as a comedian in 1925. For what studio?

84. What is the name of the character W. C. Fields plays in "The Bank Dick"?

85. Donald Duck made his first appearance in a cartoon entitled "The Wise Little Hen." What is Donald's role in another of his early films, "The Band Concert" (1935)?

86. Joan Crawford was a hit in "Our Dancing Daughters." What dance does she do in a highlight of the film?

87. What is the title of the first Mickey Mouse cartoon utilizing a sound track?

88. Humphrey Bogart won the best actor Academy Award for his role in what movie?

89. Who was Joan Crawford's first husband?

90. What role does Joan Crawford play in "Rain"?

91. In what Disney movie is the music of "The Nutcracker Suite" and "Night on Bald Mountain" heard, and who conducts the orchestra?

92. Who has the female lead opposite Humphrey Bogart in "Key Largo"?

93. In what movie did Clark Gable win the Academy Award as best actor?

94. What was the paradise land in Tibet mentioned in "Lost Horizon" called?

95. The de Guiche Sisters were known by what names in their movie careers?

96. Who portrays the woman professor in "Teacher's Pet," in which Clark Gable is a self-taught newspaper city editor?

97. What is the occupation of Patch Gallagher (Clark Gable) in the 1933 MGM film "Dancing Lady," which has Joan Crawford as a burlesque performer and Franchot Tone as a playboy?

98. What is the name and occupation of the character that

Humphrey Bogart portrays in "Casablanca," a 1943 release? Who is his sweetheart in the film?

99. Lana Turner was still in her teens when she costarred with Clark Gable in a notable early 1940s movie. What was the movie?

100. Who did Keystone Cops creator Mack Sennett consider his finest comedienne?

101. Identify the song in "The Big Broadcast" (1938) which is the theme of one of today's leading entertainers.

102. Do you know the screen acting name of Betty Jane Thornburg?

103. Scarlett O'Hara went into business and sold what, in "Gone with the Wind"?

104. What is Clark Gable's final line in "Gone with the Wind"?

105. What does Joan Crawford find out that makes her afraid, in "Sudden Fear"?

106. Who portrayed Louella Parsons in "Hollywood Hotel"?

107. Who played the role of Jesse James in the 1939 movie of that name?

108. What was the name of the first dog to become a film star?

109. Do you know the occupation of Philip Marshall, portrayed by Charles Laughton in "The Suspect"?

110. In what movie did Elizabeth Taylor make her screen debut?

111. In what picture did Eddie Cantor make his screen debut, in 1926?

112. What song, named after a country, was featured in the Walt Disney movie "Saludos Amigos," in 1943?

113. Who starred as Mr. Chips in "Goodbye Mr. Chips"? What is the occupation of Mr. Chips?

114. Name the star who introduced the song "Night and Day" on the screen.

115. Who appears as Professor Higgins in the 1938 MGM release "Pygmalion," adapted from Shaw's play of that name?

116. Who starred as a wild flapper in the silent "Our Dancing Daughters," released by MGM in 1928?

117. Walter Long was the "heavy" featured in the 1930 movie "Pardon Us." Name the comic team that starred in the picture.

118. What role did Scotty Beckett play in the 1947 Columbia movie "The Jolson Story"?

119. What mid-1940s Paramount release, directed by John Farrow, starred Alan Ladd, Brian Donlevy, William Bendix, and Barry Fitzgerald?

120. Name the Vitagraph star regarded as the movies' first comic fat man.

121. In proper order, name at least two of the three actors who portrayed the Frankenstein monster in these movies: "Frankenstein" (1931), "The Ghost of Frankenstein" (1942), and "Frankenstein Meets the Wolf Man" (1943).

122. What actress was known as "the girl with the bee stung lips"?

123. A 1961 United Artists release was the final motion picture for the costars, Clark Gable and Marilyn Monroe. The film's title?

124. A 1942 movie, starring Judy Garland, brought back into popularity a song that had been out for 25 years and had been a favorite of Al Jolson, Eddie Cantor, Sophie Tucker, and Belle Baker. The title of the movie is the title of the song. What is it?

125. What actor gained considerable recognition for his role of Duke Mantee in the 1936 film "Petrified Forest"?

126. Who plays the role of German Field Marshal Rommel in "The Desert Fox"?

127. Name the actress featured in the elaborate bathing scene in "Male and Female," a silent film of the post-World War I era.

128. Who portrays gangster-gambler Arnold Rothstein in "King of the Roaring '20s—The Story of Arnold Rothstein"?

129. Who portrays the "Invisible Man" in the 1933 movie of that title, and what is his occupation?

130. Do you know the silent screen heroine who starred in serials that included "Plunder" and "The Black Secret"?

131. Greta Garbo stars in a 1939 movie in which she plays the role of a Communist in Paris. The picture marked her comedy debut. Its title?

132. Who plays the mummy in "The Mummy's Hand" (1940)?

133. What famous role was played by these four actors: King Baggot, John Barrymore, Fredric March, and Spencer Tracy?

134. Gregory Peck Won an Academy Award for his leading

role in the 1962 movie "To Kill a Mockingbird." What part does he play and in what community does the character live?

135. Actors Gabriel Dell, Leo Gorcey, Huntz Hall, Bernard Punsley, Bobby Jordan, and Billy Halop performed together. What was the group called?

136. Name the actor who costarred with five-year-old Shirley Temple in "Little Miss Marker."

137. "The Great Ziegfeld" won an Academy Award as the best movie of 1936, and its leading lady, Luise Rainer, also won an Academy Award for her portrayal of Anna Held. Who played the role of Flo Ziegfeld?

138. What role does Juanita Hall play in the 1958 production of "South Pacific"?

139. Wallace Beery and Robert Newton respectively portrayed Long John Silver in the 1934 and 1950 releases of "Treasure Island." What two young actors played Jim Hawkins in these films?

140. Who are the top three stars in "The Philadelphia Story"?

141. "The African Queen" stars Humphrey Bogart as Charlie Allnut. Who portrays Rose?

142. "Notorious," produced and directed by Alfred Hitchcock, contains what may be the longest kiss ever seen on the movie screen. Who is involved in it?

143. Who played the roles of Blondie and Dagwood on radio and in the movies?

144. Steve Allen had a leading role in which he took the part of a popular bandleader. Name the picture.

145. A 1933 Paramount production of "Alice in Wonderland" featured a number of well-known actors. Among them: Ned Sparks, Leon Errol, Cary Grant, Edward Everett Horton, Jack Oakie, and Gary Cooper. An actor not mentioned here is————.

146. One of the better motion pictures of 1948 was "The Naked City," starring Barry Fitzgerald as Lieutenant Dan Muldoon and Howard Duff as Frank Niles. Who produced the picture?

147. In the Academy Award-winning movie "The Lost Weekend," Don Birnam (Ray Milland) is thrown out of a nightclub by the bouncer. Why?

148. What was the name of the horse ridden by movie cowboy Tom Mix?

149. What comedy team starred in "Animal Crackers," "Duck Soup," and "A Night at the Opera"?

150. The 1942 movie "Mrs. Miniver" won an Academy Award as the best picture of the year, and Greer Garson won an Academy Award for her portrayal of Mrs. Miniver. Who played the role of Mr. Miniver?

151. Roddy McDowall starred in a movie in the early 1940s in which he played the part of a boy in love with a horse. The picture?

152. Name the motion picture in which Al Jolson first sang "Sonny Boy."

153. The musical "The Shocking Miss Pilgrim" was released in 1947 by 20th Century-Fox. It is about a young lady who enters the business world of the 1870s. Who portrays Cynthia Pilgrim?

154. Name the actress who won an Academy Award for her performance as Lola Delaney in the 1952 movie "Come Back, Little Sheba."

155. The 1944 movie "National Velvet" is about a girl who rides a horse to victory in England's Grand National Steeplechase. What is the name of the girl in the picture and who portrays her? What is the name of the horse?

156. Shirley Booth played the role of Miss Duffy on radio, but who portrayed Miss Duffy in the 1945 Paramount movie "Duffy's Tavern"?

157. Name the child actor of the 1930s who starred in the movies "David Copperfield" and "Little Lord Fauntleroy."

158. Name the man called the czar of the motion-picture industry.

159. Who plays the title role of the water carrier who becomes a hero in the 1939 movie "Gunga Din"?

160. Jane Wyman won an Academy Award for her portrayal of Belinda in "Johnny Belinda" (1948). What is Belinda's last name and how is she handicapped?

161. Name the actress who costarred with John Boles in "Stella Dallas," with Joel McCrea in "Union Pacific," and with Henry Fonda in "The Lady Eve."

162. "Carefree" (1938) has a scene in which a dance called the "Yam" is introduced. Who are the two dancers who perform it?

163. Early in this century, Marie Dressler starred in "Tillie's

Punctured Romance." In the film, she held a baby to her heart. In real life, who was the baby?

164. What was the first full-length animated motion picture released by Walt Disney?

165. What comedian has been in these movies: "Never Say Die," "Nothing but the Truth," "Let's Face It," and "Where There's Life"?

166. Identify the two stars of the movie "Tortilla Flat" (1942).

167. "The Trail of the Lonesome Pine" (1936), filmed around Lake Tahoe and released by Paramount, is the first full-length motion picture to be photographed in what way? Sylvia Sydney and Henry Fonda are the stars.

168. In what 1935 MGM movie was the song "When I Grow Too Old to Dream" introduced? Who wrote it?

169. What causes Scott Carey (played by Grant Williams) to shrink in "The Incredible Shrinking Man"?

170. "Citizen Kane" is believed by many to be based on the life of an actual person. Who?

171. Who said, "Beulah, peel me a grape"?

172. In the 1932 Academy Award-winning film "Grand Hotel," Greta Garbo plays the part of Grusinskaya. What is Grusinskaya's occupation and who falls in love with her?

173. Identify the first talking movie with Mary Pickford.

174. What was the occupation of Andy Hardy's father in the Andy Hardy movie series? Who portrayed Andy and his father?

175. What was the first Silly Symphony animated cartoon?

176. Who sang "I've Got a Heartful of Music" in the movie "The Cowboy from Brooklyn," made in the late 1930s?

177. Ingrid Bergman stars as Anastasia in the 1956 movie of that name. Who plays the part of the empress?

178. Who produced and directed "Stalag 17" (1953)?

179. Who played the role of Scattergood Baines in the movies?

180. Can you provide the first names of three of the five winners of the best actor Academy Awards from 1960 to 1964?

181. Name two of the top three stars of "The Strawberry Blonde" (1941).

182. Name the group that starred in these movies: "Lazy

Days," "Boxing Gloves," "Bouncing Babies," "Bear Shooters," and "A Tough Winter."

183. Walt Disney's "Make Mine Music" is a full-length animated movie released in the mid-1940s. In the picture, who does the voice of Willie the Whale?

184. What is the title of the Paramount movie that features these songs: "I Hear Music," "Manana," and "Lovable Sort of Person"?

185. What was cowboy sidekick George (Gabby) Hayes known as when he appeared with Bill Boyd in the Hopalong Cassidy movie series?

186. Who narrates Walt Disney's animated movie "Peter and the Wolf"? What is the name of the duck in the film?

187. Who played the role of Snowshoes in the 1938 movie "Charlie Chan in Egypt"?

188. One of the stars of the Academy Award-winning movie "The Best Years of Our Lives" is Fredric March, who portrays a man named Al Stephenson. What is Al's civilian occupation and what rank does he hold when he returns from service?

189. Name the three members of one family who appeared in the 1932 movie "Rasputin."

190. Bette Davis won an Academy Award for her role in what 1935 Warner Brothers film?

191. Peter Lorre, Boris Karloff, and Bela Lugosi are in the cast of the 1940 movie "You'll Find Out." Another actor, however, is the star. Who?

192. In the 1954 movie "Suddenly," who plays the role of a psychotic killer who tries to assassinate the President?

193. James Cagney won an Academy Award for his portrayal of George M. Cohan in "Yankee Doodle Dandy" (1942). Who portrays George's father, Jerry Cohan, in the film?

194. Who played the role of Louisiana Governor Jimmie Davis in the 1947 movie "Louisiana"?

195. In the movie classic "The Wizard of Oz," who is Professor Marvel?

196. What does W. C. Fields give away in the comedy film "The Pharmacist"?

197. In different "Road" films, who played the roles of George Cochran, Seat Sweeney, and Jeff Peters?

198. What is the movie scene when these words are spoken:

"The whole world will pay to see this ... We're millionaires, boys. I'll share it with all of you ..."?

199. What is Shirley Temple's middle name?

200. Ann Rutherford played what role in many of the Andy Hardy movies?

201. What is the name of the wire-hair terrier in "The Thin Man," starring William Powell and Myrna Loy?

202. What was the first film of the James Bond series and who portrayed the chief villain?

203. Identify "Hal" in the movie "2001: A Space Odyssey."

204. The Marx Brothers made their first screen appearance in what picture?

205. Rand Brooks, Andy Clyde, Jay Kirby, and George (Gabby) Hayes were among what cowboy's sidekicks?

206. What is the name of the sheriff portrayed by Gary Cooper in "High Noon"?

207. Who sings "It's a Great Day for the Irish" in "Little Nellie Kelly"?

208. Who was the movie comedian famous for saying "Woo, woo"?

209. Can you remember who portrays either Mr. Starrett or Mrs. Starrett in the 1953 movie "Shane"? Alan Ladd stars as Shane.

210. Who portrays Sergeant Alvin York's sweetheart, Gracie Williams, in "Sergeant York" (1941)?

211. Bob Steele played in nearly two hundred movies of what type?

212. Gene Polar, P. Dempsey Tabler, James Pierce, and Herman Brix all portrayed what screen hero?

213. In what movie starring Edward G. Robinson was the question asked, "Is this the end of Rico?"

214. In which one of the "Road" movies do Dorothy Lamour, Bing Crosby, and Bob Hope appear as old people?

215. "My little plum" was W. C. Fields's pet name for whom in "Poppy"?

216. In the 1951 movie "Death of a Salesman," who plays the role of the salesman, Willy Loman?

217. The Cisco Kid's horse was named———.

218. "Your private life has got to be an open book" is a line in a mid-1930s movie. Who replied, "It is ... I'm just lookin' for somebody to read it"? What is the title of the picture?

219. What is the sequel to "Mrs. Miniver"?

220. Al St. John played roles of sidekicks in a great number of western movies. His nickname?

221. In what movie does Groucho Marx, as Ambassador Firefly, pick up a doughnut from a table and dunk it in someone's coffee cup at another table?

222. What is the name of the goldfish in Walt Disney's "Pinocchio"?

223. What is W. C. Fields's name in "You Can't Cheat an Honest Man"?

224. Who portrays Kitty Foyle in the movie of that name?

225. What is the 1936 film starring Gary Cooper in which the word "pixilated" is used several times?

226. In "The Unholy Three," how does Lon Chaney unwittingly reveal his true identity while on a witness stand?

227. Mr. Chipping, portrayed by Robert Donat, was the leading character in a picture that was released in 1939. Its title?

228. What actress, now in her forties, appears in these movies: "The Holy Terror," "Boy Friend," "Youth Will Be Served," and "Her First Beau"?

229. In what movie of the 1930s does Paul Muni portray a former war hero who is framed for a robbery he didn't commit and soon finds himself in a chain gang?

230. Baby LeRoy drops a watch in molasses, whereupon his mother says, "I don't know why he's behaving like this; you should see him when he's alone." The man whose watch was dropped replies, "Yes, I'd like to catch him when he's alone!" Who says that?

231. What is the title of the movie in which Charlie Chaplin falls in love with a blind flower girl?

232. Gene Kelly had been on Broadway but first danced in the movies with Judy Garland in what picture?

233. Name the actress who was famous for wearing a sarong.

234. Who portrayed the English butler Ruggles in the mid-1930s movie "Ruggles of Red Gap"?

235. "Bonnie and Clyde" contains a part of what 1930s film in which what female sings "We're in the Money"?

236. What cowboy's horse was called the Wonder Horse?

237. Name the well-known actress who appears in these movies: "Jezebel," "The Man Who Came to Dinner," "Marked Woman," and "Mr. Skeffington."

238. Who won Academy Awards for roles in "Captains Courageous" and "Boys Town"?

239. The 1909 movie "Gertie the Dinosaur" was the first of what type of picture?

240. Smiley Burnette appeared in about 200 western movies, playing a large number of times—more than 80—whose sidekick?

241. Who was the actress who played the role of an aristocratic and wealthy society woman in many Marx Brothers movies?

242. What was the Wallace Beery-Marie Dressler follow-up movie to "Min and Bill"?

243. In the movie "Kid Galahad," who says to his kid sister, "I tried to keep you decent, didn't I? Sent you to a convent—kept you away from guys"?

244. What comedian appears in "Whistling in Brooklyn," "The Fuller Brush Man," and "Susan Slept Here"?

245. What film company began the Movietone Newsreel with sound, in 1927?

246. What "rock" song is featured in the mid-1950s movie "The Blackboard Jungle"?

247. "Gif me a viskey, ginger ale on the side—and don't be stingy, baby" was the first sentence what noted actress spoke in sound movies? What was the movie (1930)?

248. In what mid-1940s movie is the song "Zip-a-Dee-Do-Dah"?

249. In the movies, who said: "You say you want to get hold of Mrs. Potter—I don't know, she's awfully ticklish"?

250. Name the producer who joined with actors Douglas Fairbanks and Charles Chaplin and actress Mary Pickford to form United Artists.

251. "Buttons and Bows" won an Academy Award for best film song of 1948. Name the movie in which it appeared.

252. Do you know the name of Hopalong Cassidy's horse?

253. Name the actor in these films: "House of Strangers," "The Ten Commandments," "Brother Orchid," and "Barbary Coast."

254. "It would please the faculty if you would throw away your cigar, professor" is a line in "Horse Feathers." Who responded, "The faculty might as well keep their seats—there'll be no diving for this cigar"?

255. Frank Sinatra sings "Time After Time" in what mid-1940s movie?

256. What was Walt Disney's next feature film—a cartoon—after "Snow White"?

257. Who said these noted lines: "Wait till you hear this, mama ... When I'm a hit I'm going to take you to Coney Island and I'm going to buy you the prettiest black silk dress that'll make a noise when you walk. Will you like that, mama?"

Answers

1. Josephine Dillon, Rhea Langham, Carole Lombard, Sylvia Hawkes, and Kay Spreckels.
2. 76. He was born in 1899.
3. "Beach" ... "Hour" ... "Song."
4. "All Quiet on the Western Front."
5. Lew Lehr.
6. Deanna Durbin, Barbara Read, and Nan Grey.
7. Stan Laurel and Oliver Hardy.
8. Frank Morgan.
9. Both brown.
10. "King."
11. Anna May Wong.
12. Wallace Beery and Jackie Cooper, respectively.
13. "The Gunfighter."
14. "Dracula."
15. Harold Lloyd.
16. The Phantom, in versions of "Phantom of the Opera."
17. Erich von Stroheim.
18. Joan Crawford.
19. "Algiers," a 1938 picture.
20. "Giant."
21. Sing Sing prison.
22. Betty Grable was Jenny and June Haver was Rosie.
23. Detective Sam Spade.
24. MGM.
25. Jane Withers.
26. "The Merry Widow."
27. "She Done Him Wrong" (1933).
28. Jack Benny.
29. He attempts to eat a shoe and lace, treating the shoe as meat and the lace as spaghetti.
30. It caused his upper lip to be partly paralyzed, resulting in a tightly set mouth and a lisp.
31. Constance Bennett.
32. Mae Clarke.
33. A tree or plant of manlike build, with sap instead of blood and thorns on the ends of its arms in place of fingers.

34. "Captain January."
35. John Gilbert and Greta Garbo.
36. Lon Chaney.
37. Tom Mix.
38. Will Rogers.
39. "Three Wise Fools," featuring Margaret O'Brien.
40. A 1930 remake of "The Unholy Three."
41. "The Gold Rush."
42. William S. Hart.
43. Stenographer.
44. Richard Dix.
45. Broncho Billy.
46. That of Pee Wee, the small boy hit by a car as his pal Whitey (Mickey Rooney) is leaving Boys Town.
47. "Never Give a Sucker an Even Break."
48. Donald Duck.
49. Joseph Cotten.
50. May McAvoy and John Gilbert.
51. That of a dumb hoodlum.
52. "On the Banks of the Wabash."
53. Charles Laughton.
54. "It Had to Be You."
55. They are the voices of the six speaking dwarfs, with Pinto Colvig doing both Grumpy and Sleepy. Dopey does not speak.
56. Mr. Micawber.
57. Mack Sennett.
58. "Three Little Pigs."
59. "Philadelphia will do." Fields was born in Philadelphia.
60. Baby LeRoy.
61. "Gone with the Wind" (1939).
62. James Cagney and Pat O'Brien.
63. Hal Roach.
64. "The Gay Divorcee."
65. "It ain't heavy—I can hold it myself."
66. Clark Gable.
67. Sister and brother.
68. Fred Astaire.
69. He is a rabbit, in "Bambi."
70. "The Wizard of Oz"; Judy Garland.
71. Elmo Lincoln.
72. "The Treasure of the Sierra Madre."
73. W. C. Fields.
74. Charles Laughton; Trevor Howard.
75. Dick Powell.
76. Charlton Heston, in the title role.
77. Cary Grant; Shirley Temple.
78. "Mildred Pierce" (1945).
79. Alan Ladd.
80. Singapore.
81. Jiminy Cricket.
82. "Flubber" (for flying rubber).

83. Hal Roach.
84. Egbert Souse (pronounced Soo-say).
85. He is an ice-cream vendor who constantly interrupts conductor Mickey Mouse and the band.
86. The Charleston.
87. "Steamboat Willie" (1928).
88. "The Africa Queen" (1951).
89. Douglas Fairbanks, Jr.
90. Sadie Thompson.
91. "Fantasia," with Leopold Stokowski conducting the Philadelphia Orchestra.
92. His wife Lauren Bacall.
93. "It Happened One Night" (1934).
94. Shangri-la.
95. Lillian and Dorothy Gish.
96. Doris Day is Professor Erica Stone.
97. Gable portrays a director of musical shows.
98. In this film, Bogart portrays Rick Blaine, owner of Rick's Cafe Americain, a bar and gambling house. His sweetheart is Ingrid Bergman as Ilsa Lund Laszlo.
99. "Honky Tonk."
100. Mabel Normand.
101. "Thanks for the Memory," Bob Hope's theme.
102. Betty Hutton.
103. Lumber.
104. "Frankly, my dear, I don't give a damn." He says this to Scarlett O'Hara as he walks out on her.
105. She learns that her husband plans to murder her.
106. She played herself.
107. Tyrone Power.
108. Strongheart.
109. He worked in a tobacco shop.
110. "There's One Born Every Minute" (1942).
111. "Kid Boots," released by Paramount.
112. "Brazil."
113. Robert Donat was Mr. Chips, a Latin teacher.
114. Fred Astaire, in "The Gay Divorcee."
115. Leslie Howard.
116. Joan Crawford.
117. Laurel and Hardy.
118. That of Al Jolson as a boy.
119. "Two Years Before the Mast."
120. John Bunny.
121. Boris Karloff; Lon Chaney, Jr.; Bela Lugosi.
122. Mae Murray.
123. "The Misfits."
124. "For Me and My Gal."
125. Humphrey Bogart.
126. James Mason.
127. Gloria Swanson.
128. David Janssen.

129. Claude Rains plays the role of a mad scientist named Griffin.
130. Pearl White.
131. "Ninotchka."
132. Tom Tyler.
133. Dr. Jekyll and Mr. Hyde.
134. Lawyer Atticus Finch; the setting is Maycomb, Ala., a fictitious town.
135. The Dead End Kids, of stage and movie fame. They were also called the East Side Kids and the Bowery Boys.
136. Adolphe Menjou.
137. William Powell.
138. Bloody Mary.
139. Jackie Cooper (1934); Bobby Driscoll (1950).
140. Cary Grant, Katharine Hepburn, and James Stewart.
141. Katharine Hepburn.
142. Cary Grant and Ingrid Bergman.
143. Arthur Lake and Penny Singleton.
144. "Benny Goodman Story."
145. W. C. Fields.
146. Mark Hellinger.
147. Birnam has stolen a woman's purse and was caught.
148. Tony.
149. The Marx Brothers.
150. Walter Pidgeon is Clem Miniver.
151. "My Friend Flicka."
152. "The Singing Fool," released in 1928.
153. Betty Grable.
154. Shirley Booth.
155. Velvet Brown, played by 12-year-old Elizabeth Taylor. The horse is "The Pie."
156. Ann Thomas.
157. Freddie Bartholomew.
158. Will H. Hays, president of the Motion Picture Producers and Distributors of America, 1922–45.
159. Sam Jaffe.
160. Belinda McDonald is a deaf-mute.
161. Barbara Stanwyck.
162. Fred Astaire and Ginger Rogers.
163. Milton Berle.
164. "Snow White and the Seven Dwarfs," released in late 1937.
165. Bob Hope.
166. Spencer Tracy and Hedy Lamarr.
167. In natural color.
168. "The Night Is Young"; Sigmund Romberg and Oscar Hammerstein II.
169. He is exposed to some form of radiation while boating with his wife.
170. William Randolph Hearst.
171. Mae West, in the 1933 Paramount movie "I'm No Angel."
172. Ballet star. John Barrymore as the Baron falls in love with Grusinskaya.
173. "Coquette," released by United Artists in 1929.
174. Judge. Mickey Rooney was Andy. Lewis Stone portrayed Andy's father in all but the first film of the series.

175. "The Skeleton Dance" (1929).
176. Dick Powell.
177. Helen Hayes.
178. Jose Ferrer.
179. Guy Kibbee.
180. Burt (Lancaster), Maximilian (Schell), Gregory (Peck), Sidney (Poitier), and Rex (Harrison).
181. James Cagney, Olivia de Havilland, and Rita Hayworth.
182. Our Gang.
183. Nelson Eddy.
184. "Dancing on a Dime."
185. "Windy."
186. Sterling Holloway; Sonia.
187. Stepin Fetchit.
188. He is a banker who comes home a sergeant.
189. John, Ethel, and Lionel Barrymore.
190. "Dangerous."
191. Kay Kyser.
192. Frank Sinatra, as John Baron.
193. Walter Huston.
194. Governor Davis himself.
195. The Wizard, portrayed by Frank Morgan.
196. Large vases.
197. Bing Crosby.
198. Carl Denham, upon capturing King Kong in the movie "King Kong.'
199. Jane.
200. Andy's girl friend, Polly Benedict.
201. Asta.
202. "Dr. No," with Joseph Wiseman as the evil doctor.
203. The spaceship computer.
204. "The Cocoanuts" (1929).
205. Hopalong Cassidy's.
206. Will Kane.
207. Judy Garland.
208. Hugh Herbert.
209. Van Heflin; Jean Arthur.
210. Joan Leslie
211. Westerns.
212. Tarzan.
213. "Little Caesar."
214. "Road to Utopia."
215. His adopted daughter, portrayed by Rochelle Hudson.
216. Fredric March.
217. Diablo.
218. Mae West; "Go West, Young Man."
219. "The Miniver Story."
220. Fuzzy.
221. "Duck Soup."
222. Cleo.
223. Larson E. Whipsnade.
224. Ginger Rogers.

225. "Mr. Deeds Goes to Town."
226. He's disguised as an old woman but his voice lapses into its normal pitch.
227. "Goodbye, Mr. Chips."
228. Jane Withers.
229. "I Am a Fugitive from a Chain Gang."
230. W. C. Fields.
231. "City Lights."
232. "For Me and My Gal."
233. Dorothy Lamour.
234. Charles Laughton.
235. "Gold Diggers of 1933"; Ginger Rogers.
236. Tom Mix's horse Tony.
237. Bette Davis.
238. Spencer Tracy.
239. Animated cartoon.
240. Gene Autry's.
241. Margaret Dumont.
242. "Tugboat Annie."
243. Edward G. Robinson.
244. Red Skelton.
245. Fox.
246. "Rock Around the Clock," with Bill Haley and the Comets.
247. Greta Garbo; "Anna Christie" (1930).
248. "Song of the South."
249. Groucho Marx, in "The Cocoanuts."
250. D. W. Griffith.
251. "The Paleface."
252. Topper.
253. Edward G. Robinson.
254. Groucho Marx.
255. "It Happened in Brooklyn."
256. "Pinocchio."
257. Al Jolson in "The Jazz Singer," first full-length movie with talking.

LITERATURE

1. Who wrote: "War talk by men who have been in a war is always interesting; whereas moon talk by a poet who has not been in the moon is likely to be dull"?
2. In literature, what is Edmond Dantes called?
3. Who wrote: "You can't appreciate home till you've left it, money till it's spent, your wife till she's joined a woman's club, nor Old Glory till you see it hanging on a broomstick on the shanty of a consul in a foreign town"?
4. Who wrote: "Single men in barracks don't grow into plaster saints"?
5. Fictional hero Frank Merriwell attended what university?
6. According to a Persian proverb, "He who knows, and knows not that he knows, is . . ." Complete the line.
7. "The course of true love never did run smooth" is in which of Shakespeare's works?
8. Who said: "It's no disgrace t' be poor, but it might as well be"?
9. In which of his writings did Charles Dickens say "There are books of which the backs and covers are by far the best parts"?
10. Do you know the origin of the quotation "I pray God to keep me from being proud"?
11. What is Sherlock Holmes's home address?
12. Who wrote: "Stick close to your desks and never go to sea / And you all may be Rulers of the Queen's Navee"?
13. Who is the principal literary character associated with Sleepy Hollow?
14. What American essayist and humorist wrote: "One of the most striking differences between a cat and a lie is that a cat has only nine lives"?
15. Name the book in which author Conan Doyle invented Sherlock Holmes.
16. Who is first mate on the "Pequod" in "Moby Dick"?
17. Who was the villain in "Tom Sawyer"?
18. Who is the thief in "Silas Marner"?

19. What is the moral of the fable about the Hare and the Tortoise?

20. Do you know the moral of Aesop's fable about the goose that laid a golden egg every day?

21. Capulet is the last name of a well-known heroine. Her first name?

22. Name the creator of fictional detective Philo Vance.

23. In an Aesop's fable, who says, "I'd rather have common food in safety than dates and nuts in the midst of danger"?

24. In an Aesop fable, whom do ants ask, "Did you not store food away last summer for use now?"

25. The following is from what famous thriller: "I had my head in, and was about to open the lantern, when my thumb slipped upon the tin fastening, and the old man sprang up in the bed, crying out—'Who's there?' "

26. From what book is the following: "About midnight Joe awoke, and called the boys. There was a brooding oppressiveness in the air that seemed to bode something. The boys huddled themselves together and sought the friendly companionship of the fire . . ."?

27. Who wrote in "It Is Later Than You Think," "Ah! the clock is always slow / It is later than you think"?

28. Who found and dug up the treasure in "Treasuer Island"?

29. "Dracula," by Bram Stoker, begins with a story related from whose journal?

30. According to the classic French tale, the twin brother of what king was kept in an iron mask?

31. In which of Shakespeare's writings is the line, "A light wife doth make a heavy husband"?

32. Who is the author of these lines from "Ichabod": "When faith is lost, when honor dies / The man is dead"?

33. "Wee Willie Winkie," "The Strange Ride of Morrowbie Jukes," and "Rhyme of the Three Captains" are all writings of what author?

34. Edward L. Stratemeyer wrote the "Rover Boys" series of stories. What was his pen name?

35. Jane Mast was a pen name adopted by what well-known actress?

36. Ring Lardner wrote, "Mother set facing the front of the train, as it makes her giddy to ride backwards. I set

facing her, which does not affect me." In which of his stories does this appear?

37. "For Whom the Bell Tolls" is a story of a civil war in what country?

38. Who created the "Dr. Kildare" stories?

39. What is the sequel to Lewis Carroll's "Alice's Adventures in Wonderland"?

40. "Music is Love in search of a word" is found in which of Sidney Lanier's writings?

41. Do you know the occupation of Dodsworth, in the book of that name by Sinclair Lewis?

42. Stuffy Pete and the Old Gentleman are characters in what story by O. Henry?

43. For what is the White Rabbit searching in "Alice's Adventures in Wonderland"?

44. Many of the best-known fables are credited to Aesop. Who was he?

45. What did writers Frederick Van Rensselaer Dey and Thomas C. Harbaugh have in common?

46. In 1938, Eric Knight wrote a dog story for his daughter. It was published as a short story and later expanded into a book for children. What is the book's title?

47. Name the detective character created more than four decades ago by cousins Frederic Dannay and Manfred B. Lee.

48. What is the occupation of George and Lennie in John Steinbeck's "Of Mice and Men"?

49. Where is "The Teahouse of the August Moon" set?

50. Who first used the name "Shangri-la"?

51. "The People of the Abyss," by Jack London, depicts slum life in what city?

52. Upton Sinclair's book "The Jungle" was about bad conditions where?

Answers

1. Mark Twain, in "Life on the Mississippi."
2. The Count of Monte Cristo.
3. O. Henry.
4. Rudyard Kipling, in "Tommy."
5. Yale.
6. ". . . asleep, wake him."
7. "A Midsummer Night's Dream."
8. Frank McKinney (Kin) Hubbard, in "The Sayings of Abe Martin."

9. "Oliver Twist" (chapter 14).
10. Samuel Pepys's "Diary," about three centuries ago.
11. 221-B Baker Street, London, England.
12. William S. Gilbert, in "H.M.S. Pinafore."
13. Ichabod Crane.
14. Mark Twain, in "Pudd'nhead Wilson's Calendar."
15. "A Study in Scarlet."
16. Starbuck.
17. Injun Joe.
18. Dunstan Cass.
19. "Slow and steady wins the race."
20. "It takes time to gain success." The owner killed the goose to get all the gold at once.
21. Juliet, of Shakespeare's "Romeo and Juliet."
22. S. S. Van Dine.
23. The country mouse, in the fable "The Town Mouse and the Country Mouse."
24. A grasshopper who is begging for food in the winter because he danced and sang during the summer instead of storing food.
25. "The Tell-Tale Heart," by Edgar Allan Poe.
26. "The Adventures of Tom Sawyer," by Mark Twain.
27. Robert W. Service.
28. Ben Gunn.
29. Jonathan Harker's.
30. Louis XIV.
31. "The Merchant of Venice."
32. John Greenleaf Whittier.
33. Rudyard Kipling.
34. Arthur M. Winfield. He had numerous other pseudonyms for other stories.
35. Mae West.
36. "The Golden Honeymoon."
37. Spain.
38. Max Brand (real name, Frederick Faust).
39. "Through the Looking Glass." The author's real name was not Lewis Carroll but Charles Lutwidge Dodgson.
40. "The Symphony."
41. Auto manufacturer.
42. "Two Thanksgiving Day Gentlemen."
43. A pair of white kid gloves and a fan.
44. A Greek slave. He is believed to have lived about 620—560 B.C.
45. Each of them wrote hundreds of Nick Carter detective stories.
46. "Lassie Come Home."
47. Ellery Queen.
48. They are migratory farm laborers.
49. The Pacific island of Okinawa.
50. James Hilton in his novel "Lost Horizon." Shangri-la is the name of an imaginary area in the mountains of Tibet.
51. London, England.
52. The stockyards of Chicago.

RADIO

1. Who was the long time star of "The Fleischmann Hour"?
2. In 1947, a radio star kidded his network and its vice-presidents, and he was cut off the air for 25 seconds. Identify him.
3. What did Don Carney do on radio?
4. Who was director of the "Good Will Court"?
5. What news commentator was known for his "voice of doom" approach to the news?
6. Brenda and Cobina were characters on what program during the late 1930s?
7. What was unusual about the physical appearance of broadcaster Floyd Gibbons?
8. L. A. (Speed) Riggs was featured on "Your Hit Parade." What did he do?
9. What was the name of the Lone Ranger's nephew?
10. What serial personality supposedly mailed simulated gold Solar Scout badges and a handbook to listeners who sent in a green triangle from a Cream of Wheat box top?
11. Who organized the NBC Symphony and became its first conductor in 1937?
12. What kind of news did Jimmy Fidler report?
13. What was the name of the detective series that starred William Gargan?
14. Parkyakarkas was a character first heard is 1936, on whose program?
15. Who was called the "Street Singer"?
16. Frank Crummit and Julia Sanderson, husband and wife, starred on a show sponsored by a cigar manufacturing firm. Name the company.
17. "Calling Dr. Brent . . . surgery" was heard at the beginning of each episode of a popular serial. Its title?
18. Squire Skimp was a character on what program?
19. Who was hostess of what 90-minute weekly variety show that began in late 1950 on NBC?

20. What are the call letters of the early station in Pittsburgh?

21. What important part did Pierre Andre play on the "Little Orphan Annie" programs?

22. In 1930, the "Town Crier" broadcasts went on the air. Who was the Town Crier?

23. Who was the longtime announcer on the "Fibber McGee and Molly" show?

24. What was the earlier name of the network now known as the American Broadcasting Company?

25. Name the little girls who sang on the "Horn and Hardart Children's Hour" and on another program under sponsorship of Thrivo Dog Food.

26. What did Walter Winchell regularly say at the beginning of his Sunday night news program?

27. Senator Ford, Harry Hershfield, and Joe Laurie, Jr., tried to top jokes sent in by listeners to "Can You Top This?" Who told the jokes for the listeners?

28. The "Straight Shooters Club" for young listeners was associated with what cowboy?

29. Who was the long time moderator of "Vox Pop"?

30. What was the original name of Tom Breneman's "Breakfast in Hollywood" show?

31. "The Sweetest Story Ever Told" was the theme music for what early serial?

32. What did Jimmy Durante say at the conclusion of his weekly program?

33. Smilin' Ed McConnell was a favorite of millions of children. What did Smilin' Ed call his program?

34. Keenan Wynn once played the part of a character named Shrevie. Name the show and Shrevie's line of work.

35. What was the full name of newscaster H. V. Kaltenborn?

36. Nielsen is a leading rating service for TV shows. Who was the number one rater of network radio programs some years ago?

37. What radio orchestra specialized in musical sleighbells?

38. Who played the part of Baby Snooks's "Daddy"?

39. "The Quiz Kids" began on NBC in 1940. What company sponsored the weekly program?

40. "A box of Mars bars and two tickets to next week's

production" were prizes given to losing contestants on what quiz show?

41. Who played the role of Miss Duffy on "Duffy's Tavern"?

42. "You'll be sorry" was often shouted from the audience of what show?

43. Ezra Stone and Jackie Kelk appeared on a popular show. What roles did they have and what was the show?

44. Name the food product that sponsored Jack Benny on radio for years.

45. "Here's Morgan" was a five-night-a-week program that first brought national recognition to what person?

46. Orson Welles, Bill Johnstone, and Arthur Vinton all played the same radio character. Who did they portray?

47. Who was the mind reader who had a network show some years ago?

48. Who were the characters portrayed by Freeman Gosden and Charles Correll just before the two became Amos 'n' Andy?

49. Dr. Jim Brent was a name familiar to listeners of what serial?

50. In 1938, a broadcast of H. G. Wells's "The War of the Worlds" frightened thousands of persons who believed the Earth was being invaded by Martians. Name the program on which this was heard. Who produced it?

51. "Town Meetin' Tonight! Town Meetin' Tonight!" introduced what program?

52. Who was the keeper of "The Old Curiosity Shop"?

53. What was the theme music of the "Dr. Christian" program?

54. What was the name of Judy Canova's maid on Miss Canova's show?

55. Bud Collyer played the title role in an adventure program for children. What was the role?

56. Clifton Fadiman served as one of the moderators for a program that involved brainy children. Identify the program and its theme music.

57. Who wrote the serial "Pepper Young's Family"?

58. When Oscar Levant, John Kieran, Franklin P. Adams, and Clifton Fadiman went before microphones, what program was on the air?

59. Do you know the standard Vincent Lopez greeting at the opening of his many band broadcasts?

60. Ireene Wicker had a popular children's program on which she sang, recited nursery rhymes, and told stories. What was Miss Wicker called?

61. What was the name of Lum and Abner's store?

62. Who was signing off his program when these words went over the airwaves: "Yowsah ... au revoir, a fond cherrio, a bit of a tweet-tweet, God bless you . . . and pleasant dreams"?

63. A cash prize of $15 and a set of the Encyclopaedia Britannica were awards won when the experts were stumped on what quiz show?

64. Who was the star woman reporter on "Big Town"?

65. What is the brand name that completes this opening of a serial: "And now————Soap's own story—'The Right to Happiness' "?

66. The radio actress who portrayed Portia Blake Manning on "Portia Faces Life" also took the part of Belle Jones on "Lorenzo Jones." Her name?

67. What was the name of the bar frequented by Casey on "Casey, Crime Photographer"? Who was the bartender?

68. Leila Ransom was a character on a situation comedy. Who was her boyfriend?

69. What did Major Edward Bowes do on his "Amateur Hour" when he wanted a contestant to bring his act to a close?

70. Who portrayed Daisy June, Calamity Jane, Mrs. Willy Lump-Lump, and Junior's mommy on the "Red Skelton Show"?

71. What beermaker sponsored "The Danny Kaye Show" in the early 1940s?

72. Joan and Harry Davis were principal characters on what serial?

73. What was the longtime 15-minute time slot for news commentator Lowell Thomas?

74. What was the real name of the comedy character Parkyakarkas?

75. What role did Minetta Ellen play for the entire 27 years of a program?

76. Where was Bob Burns's Grandpa Snazzie supposed to have lived?

77. Willie Jefferson was a character on "Amos 'n' Andy" who was known by another name. What was it?

78. Virginia Simms and Harry Babbitt were regulars on what popular program?

79. Archibald MacLeish, Norman Corwin, and Arch Oboler were three of the top writers of dramas heard on what unsponsored program on CBS?

80. "The Lone Ranger" originated in 1933 over a station in Detroit. That station's call letters?

81. "Angel's Serenade" and "The Perfect Song" were themes of what program?

82. What was the earlier name of the serial "Joyce Jordan, M.D."?

83. Who originated "Let's Pretend"?

84. Who was the man who did the voice of Beulah?

85. Actor Arthur Hughes played the part of a serial personality who lived in Hartville. Whom did he portray?

86. "Poor Butterfly" and "How Can I Go On Without You?" were themes of what program?

87. The "First Nighter" dramas were aired from what mythical theater?

88. What was the theme song of the children's program "Big Jon and Sparky"?

89. On radio, who was Yukon King?

90. Vanilla was a dog on what leading comedy show?

91. What did Red Ryder say when he wanted his horse to go fast?

92. Joel Kupperman was one of what group of radio "kids"?

93. Dexter Franklin was whose radio boyfriend?

94. What was Dr. Jim Brent constantly asked to do in the openings of the serial "Road of Life"?

95. Name the longtime sponsor of "Fibber McGee and Molly."

96. Because of the loud sound effects at the opening of a radio program, an expression arose: "Coming on like————." Fill in the blank for the completion of the expression and the name of the program.

97. When Gracie Allen would call the announcer on the Burns and Allen show "Harry," to whom was she speaking?

98. Edgar Bergen and Charlie McCarthy were long sponsored by what brand of coffee?

99. What was the lodge to which Amos and Andy belonged?

100. A police commissioner named Weston was part of what dramatic program?

101. Frank Crumit's wife sang with him on the radio. Her name?

102. For what paper did Casey, the crime photographer, work?

103. Name the oil company that sponsored "Kaltenborn Edits the News" on radio.

104. Do you know the name of Henry Aldrich's sister?

105. The Lone Ranger's nephew was Dan Reed. Do you know the name of Dan Reed's horse?

106. The National Broadcasting Company had two radio networks, known by colors. What were they?

107. Where did the Fat Man weigh himself at the beginning of each program?

108. Frank Hummert and his wife were responsible for dozens of leading radio serials. Mrs. Hummert's first name?

109. Jack Pearl used to say, "Vass you dere, Sharlie?" What character was he playing when he said it?

110. What was the relationship between Nancy Donovan and Bill Davidson on the serial "Just Plain Bill"?

111. What was the program on which Jimmy Scribner did the voices of all the characters?

112. Complete the opening of this serial: "And now, Oxydol's own——— ———."

113. What was the comedy singing group on "The Jack Benny Program" called?

114. How did the Mysterious Traveler travel?

115. What old musical instrument of Fibber McGee's used to fall out of his overstuffed closet when he opened it, on the "Fibber McGee and Molly" show?

116. Identify either "Mr. Hush" or "Miss Hush" on the "Truth or Consequences" program.

117. Who led the orchestra on the Bell Telephone Hour?

118. What was Harry Frankel called?

119. The same actor who played the role of David Farrell on "Front Page Farrell" also portrayed Casey on "Casey, Crime Photographer." Name him.

120. Who said, "What a revoltin' development this is"?

121. Inspector Renfrew was a member of what law-enforcement body?

122. What were the occupations of Myrt and Marge on the popular serial of that name?

123. What was the name of the mayor on "Fibber McGee and Molly"?

124. Who portrayed the Lone Ranger for most of the years the program was on radio?

125. Name the show that featured dramatized stories of newspaper reporters.

126. What dramatic program used stories written by non-professionals?

127. Can you recall the name of the medical center where Dr. Jerry Malone, of the serial "Young Dr. Malone," worked?

128. On "The Fred Allen Show," what did Titus Moody say when Mr. Allen knocked on his door in Allen's Alley?

129. On "Fibber McGee and Molly," who was the husband of "Sweety Face"?

130. What did Tony Wons do on his program "Tony Wons' Scrapbook"?

131. The noted program "One Man's Family" used two theme songs over the years. Name at least one of them.

132. What was the occupation of David Farrell?

133. Who frequently told persons he was advising, "No names, please"?

134. J. Anthony Smythe played what role on "One Man's Family" for the program's entire 27-year run on radio?

135. Les Tremayne and Olan Soule teamed, at different times, with what actress on "First Nighter" dramas?

136. What serial immediately followed "Helen Trent" on CBS in two decades (the 1940s and '50s)?

137. What was the name of the telephone operator on "Fibber McGee and Molly"?

138. On radio, who said, "Oh, George, I'll bet you say that to all the girls"?

139. What was the answer to the question, "Who knows what evil lurks in the hearts of men?"

140. Who was the voice of Mickey Mouse on "The Mickey Mouse Theater of the Air"?

141. On "Amos 'n' Andy," who brought a breach of promise suit against Andy?

142. W. C. Fields exchanged insults with what "Charlie"?

143. Phil Baker, Bob Hawk, Garry Moore, and Jack Paar were all MCs of what quiz show?

144. What was the name of the maid on "The Great Gildersleeve"?

145. Larry Parks portrayed Al Jolson in the movie "The Jolson Story." Who played the part of Jolson when the movie was presented as a drama on the "Lux Radio Theatre"?

146. Mary Livingstone, Jack Benny's wife, talked a lot on their shows about what member of her family?

147. Who portrayed Hopalong Cassidy on radio?

148. Who was the first man to play the role of John Perry on the serial "John's Other Wife"?

149. "Lights out . . . e-v-e-r-y-b-o-d-y" was a repeatedly used opening for what suspense program?

150. Name the program that was a "gigantic stage on which are played a thousand dramas daily."

151. When members became 16 years of age, they were required to leave the panel of what show?

152. What was the theme song of "The Railroad Hour"?

153. Janette Davis, the Mariners, and Archie Bleyer's orchestra were featured on what daily show?

154. What was the source of the questions answered by the Answer Man?

155. Name the newspaper and radio personality who was on the air for the first time in January 1929, billed as "New York by a representative New Yorker."

156. What was the occupation of Floyd on "The Great Gildersleeve"?

157. What product sponsored "Little Orphan Annie" on radio?

158. Who was featured on "The Human Side of the News"?

159. "Lum and Abner" was set in what small Arkansas community?

160. What was the name of Tonto's horse?

161. What was the theme song of "Easy Aces"?

162. What relation were Cliff and Claudia on "One Man's Family"?

163. Who was the first star of the "Shell Chateau" show?

164. Name the detective who was a "friend of those who need a friend; enemy to those who make him an enemy."

165. "Ho-wah-ho-so-wah-ka" was the password of what children's personality?

166. The Bickersons—John and Blanche—were featured on

"The Edgar Bergen and Charlie McCarthy Show." Who portrayed them?

167. "Nowhere in the pages of history can one find a greater champion of justice" is a line from the opening of what long-run program?

168. "The monument to memory, the thought-twister" was a regular feature of what show?

169. What did the Shadow say at the conclusion of each of the programs of that name?

170. What was the name of the community in which serial heroine Joyce Jordan, M.D., practiced medicine?

171. Who had the part of Grandpappy Spears on "Lum and Abner"?

172. What role did Menasha Skulnik play on "The Goldbergs"?

173. Name the serial heroine "who fell in love with and married Broadway matinee idol Larry Noble."

174. What was unusual about the way the theme of "The Romance of Helen Trent" was presented?

175. Name the Hollywood news reporter who usually began her broadcasts with "My first exclusive . . ."

176. Who owned the garage on the serial "Lorenzo Jones" at which Lorenzo worked as a mechanic?

177. Mickey Rooney portrayed Andy Hardy in the movies. Who had the role on radio?

178. What was the name of Amos Jones's little girl on "Amos 'n' Andy"?

179. Five actresses, including Mercedes McCambridge, played the role of Ruth Evans Wayne. What was Ruth called?

180. "The true-to-life story of mother love and sacrifice" brings what serial to mind?

181. What did Portland Hoffa say at the beginning of her husband's show? Her husband was Fred Allen.

182. Who was the newscaster on the partly dramatic "Wendy Warren and the News"?

183. "Whistling Rings," "Secret Decoders," and "Hike-O-Meters" were all offered by what afternoon children's show?

184. Radio serial heroine "Our Gal Sunday" was married to English Lord Henry Brinthrope. Where did they live?

185. Identify the personality who said, "That's purty good,

Johnny, but that ain't the way I heerd it. Way I heerd it, one fella sez t' other fella, s-a-a-a-y, he sez . . ."

186. What brand of soap sponsored the serial "Pepper Young's Family"?

187. Where did Ma Perkins live? Who played the role of Ma, and what washday product sponsored the program?

188. Name the "David Harum" theme song.

189. "The White Rabbit Line . . . jumps anywhere, anytime" followed the sound of a bus horn at the opening of what show?

190. Who was the wife of Lorenzo Jones?

191. What pet name did Stella Dallas call Laurel, her daughter?

192. Who was the uncle on the "Vic and Sade" program, and where did Vic and Sade and their son Rush live?

193. What program was "dedicated to the mothers and fathers of the younger generation and to their bewildering offspring"?

194. ". . . Drawn by the magnetic force, the fantastic metropolis, day and night great trains rush toward the Hudson River, sweep down its eastern bank for 140 miles, flash briefly past the long red row of tenement houses south of 125th Street . . ." is from the opening of what program?

195. Chichi and Papa David were characters in what serial story? The program was sponsored by Spic and Span and often opened with the announcer reading an inspiring message.

196. Identify the "Backstage Wife" and her actor husband.

197. Name the serial that was a "tender, human story of young married love . . . dedicated to everyone who has ever been in love."

198. Who would always answer the telephone at the opening of "Duffy's Tavern"?

Answers

1. Rudy Vallee.
2. Fred Allen.
3. As "Uncle Don," he conducted a children's program for many years.
4. A. L. Alexander.
5. Gabriel Heatter.
6. "Bob Hope Show."

7. He always wore a white patch over his left eye, which he had lost during World War I.

8. He was a tobacco auctioneer. His rapid chant was heard as part of the sponsor's (Lucky Strike cigarettes) commercials.

9. Dan Reed.

10. Buck Rogers.

11. Arturo Toscanini.

12. Hollywood and other movie gossip.

13. "Martin Kane, Private Eye."

14. Eddie Cantor's.

15. Arthur Tracy.

16. Blackstone.

17. "Road of Life."

18. "Lum and Abner."

19. "The Big Show"; Tallulah Bankhead.

20. KDKA.

21. He was the announcer, known as "Uncle Andy."

22. Alexander Woollcott.

23. Harlow Wilcox.

24. Blue Network (part of NBC).

25. Moylan Sisters (Marianne and Peggy Joan).

26. "Good evening Mr. and Mrs. North and South America and all the ships at sea. Let's go to press."

27. Peter Donald.

28. Tom Mix.

29. Parks Johnson.

30. "Breakfast at Sardi's."

31. "John's Other Wife."

32. "Good night, Mrs. Calabash, wherever you are." That was his pet name for his first wife, Jeanne, who died in 1943.

33. "Smilin' Ed McConnell and His Buster Brown Gang." The Brown Shoe Company was the sponsor.

34. "The Shadow"; cab driver. Shrevie was a friend of Lamont Cranston (The Shadow) and Margot Lane.

35. Hans von Kaltenborn.

36. Hooper.

37. The Cliquot Club Eskimos.

38. Hanley Stafford.

39. Miles Laboratories.

40. "Dr. I.Q."

41. Shirley Booth.

42. "Take It or Leave It" (later called "The $64 Question").

43. Henry Aldrich and Homer Brown; "The Aldrich Family."

44. Jell-O.

45. Henry Morgan.

46. The Shadow—and his alter ego, Lamont Cranston.

47. Dunninger.

48. "Sam and Henry," heard over WGN, Chicago (1926–28).

49. "Road of Life."

50. "Mercury Theatre of the Air"; Orson Welles.

51. "America's Town Meeting of the Air."

52. David Ross.
53. "Rainbow on the River."
54. Geranium.
55. Superman.
56. "The Quiz Kids" with the theme "School Days."
57. Elaine Carrington.
58. "Information Please."
59. "Hello everybody, Lopez speaking."
60. "The Singing Lady."
61. Jot 'Em Down Store.
62. The "Old Maestro," Ben Bernie.
63. "Information Please."
64. Lorelei Kilbourne of the "Illustrated Press."
65. "Ivory."
66. Lucille Wall.
67. Blue Note; Ethelbert.
68. Throckmorton P. Gildersleeve, on "The Great Gildersleeve."
69. He struck a large gong.
70. Harriet Hilliard.
71. Pabst.
72. "When a Girl Marries."
73. 6:45 to 7:00 P.M. (Eastern time), Monday through Friday.
74. Harry Einstein.
75. Fanny Barbour, on "One Man's Family."
76. Van Buren, Ark.
77. Lightnin'.
78. "Kay Kyser's Kollege of Musical Knowledge."
79. "Columbia Workshop."
80. WXYZ.
81. "Amos 'n' Andy."
82. "Joyce Jordan, Girl Interne."
83. Nila Mack.
84. Marlin Hurt.
85. Bill Davidson, on the program "Just Plain Bill."
86. "Myrt and Marge."
87. "Little Theater off Times Square."
88. "The Teddy Bears' Parade."
89. An Alaskan husky who belonged to Sergeant Preston of the Northwest Mounted Police on "Challenge of the Yukon."
90. "Amos 'n' Andy."
91. "Roll, Thunder, roll!"
92. He was one of the best-known Quiz Kids on radio.
93. Corliss Archer's, on the show "Meet Corliss Archer."
94. "Call surgery."
95. Johnson's Wax.
96. "Gangbusters."
97. Harry Von Zell.
98. Chase and Sanborn.
99. Mystic Knights of the Sea.
100. "The Shadow."
101. Julia Sanderson.

102. The "Morning Express."
103. Pure Oil Company.
104. Mary.
105. Victor.
106. Red and Blue.
107. In a drugstore.
108. Anne.
109. Baron Munchausen.
110. Nancy was Bill's daughter.
111. "The Johnson Family."
112. "Ma Perkins."
113. The Sportsmen.
114. By train.
115. His mandolin.
116. Jack Dempsey; Clara Bow.
117. Donald Voorhees.
118. "Singing Sam, the Barbasol Man."
119. Staats Cotsworth.
120. Chester A. Riley, on "The Life of Riley."
121. Royal Canadian Mounted Police, on "Renfrew of the Mounted."
122. They were show-business "troupers."
123. La Trivia. Gale Gordon played the role.
124. Brace Beemer.
125. "The Big Story."
126. "Dr. Christian."
127. Three Oaks.
128. "Howdy, bub!"
129. Wallace Wimple.
130. He recited poetry.
131. "Destiny Waltz"; "Patricia."
132. Newspaper reporter, on "Front Page Farrell."
133. John J. Anthony, on "The Goodwill Hour."
134. Father Henry Barbour.
135. Barbara Luddy.
136. "Our Gal Sunday."
137. Myrt.
138. Gracie Allen, to her husband George Burns.
139. "The Shadow knows."
140. Walt Disney, who also did Mickey's voice in early movie cartoons.
141. Madame Queen.
142. Charlie McCarthy, Edgar Bergen's dummy.
143. "Take It or Leave It" (later called "The $64 Question").
144. Birdie Lee Coggins.
145. Jolson himself.
146. Her mother.
147. Bill Boyd, who also played Hoppy in the movies.
148. Hanley Stafford, later Daddy Higgins on "Baby Snooks" radio shows.
149. "Lights Out."
150. "Grand Central Station."
151. "The Quiz Kids."
152. "I've Been Working on the Railroad."

153. "Arthur Godfrey Time."
154. They were submitted by listeners.
155. Walter Winchell.
156. Barber.
157. Ovaltine.
158. Edwin C. Hill.
159. Pine Ridge.
160. "Scout." Tonto, sidekick of the Lone Ranger, also had horses named "White Feller" and "Paint."
161. "Manhattan Serenade."
162. Twin brother and sister.
163. Al Jolson.
164. Boston Blackie.
165. Chief Wolf Paw.
166. Don Ameche and Frances Langford.
167. "The Lone Ranger."
168. "Dr. I.Q."
169. "The weed of crime bears bitter fruit. Crime does not pay. The Shadow knows!" (laughter).
170. Preston.
171. Chester Lauck, who also portrayed Lum Edwards.
172. Uncle David.
173. Mary Noble, "Backstage Wife."
174. The theme, "Juanita," was hummed—by Stanley Davis and Lawrence Salerno.
175. Louella Parsons.
176. Jim Barker.
177. Also Mickey Rooney. (The show was "The Hardy Family.")
178. Arbadella.
179. "Big Sister," on the serial of the same name.
180. "Stella Dallas."
181. "Oh, Mr. Allen!"
182. Douglas Edwards.
183. "Jack Armstrong, the All-American Boy."
184. Black Swan Hall, in Virginia.
185. "The Old Timer," on "Fibber McGee and Molly."
186. Camay.
187. Rushville Center. Virginia Payne played Ma for the entire 27 years of the program. Oxydol.
188. "Sunbonnet Sue."
189. The children's program, "Coast-to-Coast on a Bus."
190. Belle Jones.
191. "Lolly Baby."
192. Uncle Fletcher. The family lived in Crooper, Ill.; Vic, Sade, and Rush lived "in the little house halfway up in the next block."
193. "One Man's Family."
194. "Grand Central Station."
195. "Life Can Be Beautiful."
196. Mary and Larry Noble.
197. "When a Girl Marries."
198. Archie, the manager, portrayed by Ed Gardner.

INDIANS

1. In what present-day state of the U.S. was there a Seminole Indian war against white settlers during the late 1830s and early 1840s?
2. Name the famous Indian chief who surrendered to General George Crook at Red Cloud Agency, Nebr., in May 1877.
3. An Indian warrior and chief named Roman Nose, prominent along the Kansas border during the 1860s, belonged to what tribe?
4. Name the Cherokee Indian who invented that tribe's alphabet.
5. The Indian head or buffalo nickel succeeded what five-cent piece?
6. Geronimo, an Apache, surrendered in March 1886 to General George Crook, but he fled, surrendering in September to what other U.S. general?
7. The last major battle between Indians and U.S. troops occurred in 1890. A group of Indians were captured and brought to Wounded Knee, S.D., where some of them resisted being disarmed, resulting in the deaths of more than two hundred Indians and soldiers. To what tribe did the Indians belong?
8. General George Custer led soldiers of what cavalry in the "last stand" Battle of the Little Big Horn in 1876?
9. Who led the Sioux in their defeat of General George Custer and his troops at Little Big Horn?
10. In the early 1870s, a band of Modoc Indians, headed by Chief Kintpuash, fought to return to their former lands in what state?
11. An Indian named High Eagle was one of the last survivors of the Battle of the Little Big Horn when he died in 1952 at age 90. Of what tribe was he a member?
12. Cochise, Diablo, and Mangas Coloradas were top warriors for what tribe?
13. The city of Seattle is named after a chief of what tribe?

14. Name the Vice-President of the U.S. whose mother was a Kaw Indian.

15. Kit Carson's wife was a member of what tribe?

Answers

1. Florida.
2. Crazy Horse.
3. Southern Cheyenne.
4. Sequoya.
5. Liberty head.
6. Nelson Miles.
7. Sioux.
8. Seventh Cavalry.
9. Sitting Bull.
10. California.
11. Oglala Sioux.
12. Apache.
13. Suquamish.
14. Charles Curtis, Vice-President during the Hoover administration (1929–33).
15. Arapaho.

SPORTS

1. Who managed the St. Louis Browns in the club's final season—1953?
2. From whom did Jack Dempsey win the heavyweight title, in 1919, and in what round?
3. Within 10, how many homers did Babe Ruth hit in the two seasons of 1920 and 1921?
4. Beau Jack, a lightweight and welterweight, fought 21 main bouts in what arena from 1942 to 1949? Most of the fights were in 1943 and '44.
5. Name the only major-league baseball player to make more than 4,000 hits during his career. He was an outfielder.
6. What college football star was known as the "Galloping Ghost"?
7. Who succeeded John McGraw as manager of the New York Giants baseball club?
8. The Washington Senators finished second in the then eight-club American League in 1943 and '45. In what place did the Senators finish in 1944?
9. Adolfo Luque played what position in the major leagues?
10. Stanislaus Kiecel was a standout performer in what sport?
11. "The Sportlight" was the title of what writer's column?
12. During the 1930s and '40s, what major-league baseball team played its home games at two different parks?
13. Virgil Trucks pitched two no-hit games in 1952. Who pitched a pair of major-league no-hitters the year before?
14. Ted Lyons's final active season as a pitcher with the Chicago White Sox was 1946. Within two years, what was his first?
15. In the 1958 title game, the Baltimore Colts and New York Giants were tied 17-17 at the end of regulation play. The game ended after 8 minutes and 15 seconds of the fifth period when what player scored for the Colts?

16. Clint Courtney, in 1951, was the first major-league catcher to wear what?

17. After winning the world heavyweight boxing championship from Joe Walcott in 1952, Rocky Marciano defended the title successfully six times before retiring in 1956. In only one of the bouts did a challenger last the scheduled distance with Marciano. Who was he?

18. Identify "The House That Ruth Built."

19. Name the player in the most NFL championship contests.

20. Following are names of five all-time great baseball pitchers. Select the only right-hander of the group: Grover Cleveland Alexander, Eddie Plank, George (Rube) Waddell, Larry French, and Herb Pennock.

21. What unusual pinch hits did Chuck Essegian of the Los Angeles Dodgers make in the 1959 World Series against the Chicago White Sox?

22. The "long count" in the second Dempsey-Tunney fight, in 1927, lasted at least how many seconds, according to most observers?

23. In his 24 years of major-league baseball, Ty Cobb played with two clubs. He spent 22 seasons with the Detroit Tigers and the other 2 with what team?

24. In what year did Jesse Owens, Archie Williams, and John Woodruff win Olympic track events for the United States?

25. Name the baseball pitching star who won 152 games and lost only 41 for the Philadelphia Athletics from 1928 through '33.

26. The Soap Box Derby was first held in Akron, Ohio, in 1935, but it began a year earlier in another Ohio city. Name it.

27. Who was the quarterback who threw three touchdown passes and scored three times himself as Cleveland whipped Detroit 56-10 in the 1954 NFL title game?

28. Who managed the St. Louis Cardinals to the club's first pennant in 1926?

29. Babe Ruth hit his first and last home runs at the Polo Grounds in New York off the same pitcher. One came May 1, 1920 and the other Sept. 5, 1922. Name the pitcher.

30. In 1924, Rogers Hornsby of the St. Louis Cardinals set a high batting average for modern major-league base-

ball. Within eight points, what did Hornsby hit that year?

31. What racehorse was nicknamed "Chocolate Soldier"?

32. With what major-league baseball club was Leon (Goose) Goslin playing when he won the league batting championship in 1928?

33. What were the nicknames of baseball stars and brothers Paul and Lloyd Waner?

34. Dick Rudolph, Ray Caldwell, Hub Leonard, and Jack Quinn were four of a relative handful of baseball pitchers who were permitted in 1920 to continue using a freak pitch for the remainder of their careers. What kind of pitch was it?

35. On August 22, 1957, for the first time in a world heavyweight title boxing bout, no "official" odds were quoted on a match between then champ Floyd Patterson and his opponent. Who was the other fighter?

36. The great racehorse Man o' War did most of his running on New York State tracks. Name two of the four on which he ran.

37. Who was the Green Bay halfback, on leave from the army, who scored 19 points to lead his team to a 37-0 win over the New York Giants in the NFL championship game in 1961?

38. The 1927 New York Yankees baseball team has often been considered the best club of all time. Within 5, how many of its 154 games did the '27 Yankees win?

39. What are the first names of the three DiMaggio brothers who played major-league baseball?

40. A boxer nicknamed "The Ambling Alp" won the heavyweight title from Jack Sharkey in 1933. Identify him.

41. In what state was the first professional football game played?

42. What stable bred and owned the racehorse Citation?

43. Boxer Billy Conn was nicknamed after his home town. Give either his nickname or the city from which he hailed.

44. For what is Brooklyn Dodgers pitcher Clarence Mitchell remembered from the fifth game of the 1920 World Series against the Cleveland Indians?

45. Name the boxer known as the "Toy Bulldog." What championships did he hold?

46. The racehorse Native Dancer won 21 of the 22 races in

which he ran, finishing second on the other occasion.
What was the race and what horse defeated him?

47. In 1924, Babe Ruth played the full schedule for the
New York Yankees and led the American League with
a batting average of .378. The following year he appeared in only 98 games and batted .290. What caused
the decline?

48. What was unusual about the way the New York Giants
came out to play the second half of the 1934 championship game against the Chicago Bears?

49. The first Super Bowl was played in 1967 between what
two clubs? The score?

50. On June 9, 1956, a racehorse set a world record of
1:33 1/5 for a mile. Do you know the name of the
horse or of the track?

51. Jack Johnson won the heavyweight championship in
1908 in Sydney, Australia, from which of these fighters:
Bob Fitzsimmons, Tommy Burns, James J. Jeffries, or
Marvin Hart?

52. What exceptional fielding play was made by Bill
Wambsganss, Cleveland Indians second baseman, in the
1920 World Series against the Brooklyn Dodgers?

53. Name the quarterback who completed four touchdown
passes as Cleveland won the 1950 title game from Los
Angeles, 30-28.

54. Van Meter, Iowa, is the home town of one of baseball's
greatest pitchers, a right-hander and strikeout specialist
who entered the majors in 1936. Can you identify him
and his team?

55. What famous heavyweight championship bout was held
at the Polo Grounds in New York, on June 18, 1941? In
what round did it end?

56. In 1948, there was only one touchdown scored in the
NFL championship game, the Philadelphia Eagles
beating the Chicago Cardinals 7-0. Steve Van Buren
scored the TD, but name the lineman who recovered a
Chicago fumble that led to the score.

57. Lefty Grove, Joe Heving, and Fritz Ostermueller were
leading members of what team's pitching staff in 1939?

58. Jockey Eddie Arcaro rode five Kentucky Derby winners. In no more than five guesses, name at least two of
the horses he rode to Derby wins.

59. What was the most one-sided score in an NFL title game?

60. Name the relief pitcher who won 18 games and lost but 1 for the Pittsburgh Pirates in 1959.

61. On March 21, 1963, two boxing championships changed hands at the Los Angeles Coliseum. Luis Rodriguez won the welterweight crown from Emile Griffith. In the other bout, who beat Davey Moore and what title did he win?

62. Name at least one of the two major-league baseball pitchers who won exactly 373 regular season games.

63. In the 1928 World Series, Babe Ruth had a record-high batting average. Within 100 points, what was his average in that Series?

64. Except for Ty Cobb, only one American League baseball player batted .400 or over in more than one season. The player?

65. Who won 27 games for the Detroit Tigers the year Hal Newhouser won 29?

66. How was major-league baseball pitcher Bert Shepard handicapped?

67. Who were the first two boxers to engage in three straight title bouts?

68. Early Wynn won only one game in 1963, his final season as a major-league pitcher, but it was lifetime victory number what?

69. It was while playing in the 1911 Series that Frank Baker acquired his nickname of "Home Run." How many homers did he hit in the six games?

70. Name the National League ballplayer who most recently batted .400 or over for a full season of play.

71. Major-league baseball pitchers Spurgeon Chandler and Virgil Davis had the same nickname. Do you know it?

72. Who held three boxing championships simultaneously, and what three?

73. In 1944, an alternate name was chosen for the Philadelphia Phillies. What was it?

74. The New York Giants in 1916 won 26 consecutive baseball games, a record that still stands. In what position in the standings did the Giants finish that year?

75. Who ranks second, behind Walter Johnson, in number of shutouts pitched?

76. An important boxing match on Dec. 5, 1947, pitted Ar-

nold Raymond Cream against Joe Barrow. Both boxers were better known by other names. What are they, and who won that 1947 bout?

77. A pitcher surnamed Ford won 26 games one season and 22 the next for the New York club of the American League. Do you know his first name?

78. What do 94 and 46 represent in Babe Ruth's varied baseball career?

79. What heavyweight champ of the 1930s was nicknamed "Cinderella Man"?

80. What player has appeared in the most World Series?

81. Who scored 36 points for the Chicago Bears in the team's 61-20 triumph over the San Francisco 49ers in December 1965?

82. What right-handed batter hit the most home runs in one season for the New York Yankees?

83. The longest major-league baseball game was played between Brooklyn and Boston of the National League on May 1, 1920, ending in a 1-1 tie. Both pitchers went the distance. Name at least one of them and the number of innings played.

84. Who stole five bases and batted .500 (12 hits) in the 1931 World Series? He played for the St. Louis Cardinals against the Philadelphia Athletics.

85. What boxing title did Barney Ross win and relinquish within three months?

86. Baseball pitcher Tommy Bridges won 194 regular season and four World Series games, all for what club?

87. Name the pitcher who won three of the four games captured by the St. Louis Cardinals in the 1946 World Series. He didn't lose a game.

88. What club won Series games by scores of 16-3, 10-0, and 12-0, yet lost the Series?

89. Who refereed the Joe Louis-Max Schmeling bout for the heavyweight boxing championship, in New York on June 22, 1938?

90. Babe Ruth hit the last three home runs of his major league career—numbers 712, 713, and 714—during the 1935 season. For and against what clubs?

91. Jimmie Foxx holds the Philadelphia Athletics' club record for home runs in a season, with 58 in 1932. Name the left-handed batter who hit the most homers for the Philadelphia A's.

92. The New York Yankees won every American League pennant but one from 1936 through 1943. In what year didn't the Yankees win, and what club did?

93. Who was the last bare-knuckle world boxing champ?

94. Which of the "Four Horsemen of Notre Dame" was later commissioner of the National Football League?

95. The last batter in the only perfect World Series game, in 1956, was a pinch hitter for the Brooklyn pitcher. Name the pinch hitter and how he was put out.

96. How many errors were made in the record-long 26-inning baseball game between Boston and Brooklyn of the National League in 1920?

97. Name one of the three horses that jockey Earle Sande rode to a Kentucky Derby win.

98. Don Larsen of the New York Yankees pitched the perfect game against the Brooklyn Dodgers in the 1956 Series, winning 2-0. Who was the Dodgers' pitcher that day?

99. What major-league baseball club had a combined total of only eight home runs during the 1917 and 1918 seasons?

100. Name the major-league baseball player who made the most two-base hits during his career.

101. Name the player sold by the St. Louis Cardinals to the Chicago Cubs for $185,000 and three players—Curt Davis, Tuck Stainback, and Clyde Shoun.

102. Archie Moore won the world's light-heavyweight boxing championship in December 1952 and held it for almost eight years. Whom did he win the title from and later defeat twice in championship bouts?

103. What two cities were represented when the Packers beat the Redskins 21-6 in the 1936 NFL title game?

104. What longtime National League baseball star compiled the highest lifetime batting average?

105. What pitching record did Babe Ruth set while pitching in the 1916 World Series for the Boston Red Sox against the Brooklyn Dodgers?

106. Who was the first heavyweight boxing champion after Joe Louis?

107. Luke Appling, Roger Cramer, Joe Cronin, and Elmer Valo all played the same number of years in baseball's major leagues. Within one, how many?

108. Name the leading two-year-old racehorse of 1947 who became the top three-year-old in '48.

109. How did manager George Stallings's Boston Braves—the "Miracle Braves"—make out in World Series play?

110. Who played right field for the New York Yankees in every game of the 1942 World Series?

111. Identify the major-league pitching star nicknamed "Rapid Robert."

112. Within five points, what was Bill Dickey's lifetime major-league batting average?

113. What was the last heavyweight title bout to be scheduled for 20 rounds?

114. After his playing career had ended, Babe Ruth served part of a season—1938—as a coach with what National League club?

115. What baseball star was nicknamed "Black Mike"?

116. A game or sport started in 1927 by Garnet Carter of Tennessee became very popular during the 1930s. Identify it.

117. Before Johnny Lindell became an outfielder for the New York Yankees in 1943, what was his regular position?

118. The National League wrapped up a victory in the 1940 All-Star game in the first inning when what player hit a three-run homer?

119. In 1931, a major-league baseball pitcher hit nine home runs to set a record. Who was he?

120. George (Snuffy) Stirnweiss of the New York Yankees led the American League in batting in 1945 with a lowly .309. Who was the 37-year-old third baseman of the Chicago White Sox who finished right behind Stirnweiss?

121. What was the nickname of former major-league second baseman Joe Gordon of the New York Yankees and Cleveland Indians?

122. Name one of the two college teams that played in the football game in which the forward pass was introduced.

123. Bucky Walters won 198 and lost 160 regular season games pitching for the Philadelphia Phillies and Cincinnati Reds. However, he appeared in almost 200 other games in another position. What was it?

124. What was the uniform number of Lou Groza of the Cleveland Browns?

125. Do you know the racing colors associated with Man o' War?

126. What was unusual about the site of the championship-determining game played by the Chicago Bears and Portsmouth Spartans of the National Football League in December 1932?

127. What university did Lou Gehrig attend?

128. Max Schmeling won the vacant world's heavyweight boxing title by defeating Jack Sharkey in June 1930 at New York. How did Schmeling win that fight?

129. The 1920 Chicago White Sox finished in second place even though the club had four pitchers who each won more than 20 games. Name at least two of them.

130. August Belmont sold Man o' War at auction for $5,000 when the great racehorse was a yearling. To whom?

131. Who played second base as a member of the Philadelphia Athletics' famous "$100,000 infield"?

132. What golfer used a putter he called "Calamity Jane"?

133. In 1942, Jim Tobin of the Boston Braves established a pitcher's record that still stands. What is it?

134. Identify the boxer Rocky Marciano met in Marciano's final defense of his heavyweight championship, in April 1956.

135. Name the major-league baseball pitcher who won 24 consecutive regular season games over two seasons in the 1930s.

136. Do you know the major-league baseball club that finished in last place every year but two from 1922 through 1932?

137. For whom was Harry (Cookie) Lavagetto batting when he made the only hit off New York Yankee pitcher Floyd Bevens to bat in two runs and win the fourth game of the 1947 World Series for the Brooklyn Dodgers?

138. After Babe Ruth hit his "called shot" home run against the Chicago Cubs in the 1932 World Series, the next Yankee batter also homered. Who was he?

139. Arnold Raymond Cream and Guiseppe Antonio Berardinelli boxed against each other several times in the 1940s. What were their ring names?

140. Name the pitcher for the Boston Red Sox who won 21

games in his first season, 1945, and 25 the following
year.

141. Race horses with "Count" as part of their names were
considered the best horses of 1943 and 1952. Do you
know the full name of either?

142. What was the unusual trade between the Chicago Cubs
and the St. Louis Cardinals on May 30, 1922?

143. Baseball pitching great Carl Hubbell had three popular
nicknames. Name two of them.

144. In 1940, Cornell defeated Dartmouth in football, 7-3.
However, the score was changed to a 3-0 Dartmouth
victory when movies of the game were viewed. Why
was the score changed?

145. "Rip," "Flash," "Pepper," and "Lippy" once formed
the infield for what major-league baseball team?

146. Babe Ruth hit a record 60 home runs in 1927, topping
the old high of 59 in a season. Whose record did he
better?

147. Name the baseball club for which LeRoy (Satchel)
Paige pitched when he first played in the major leagues,
in 1948.

148. Who invented basketball?

149. Within 10 points, what was Ty Cobb's lifetime regular
season batting average?

150. Horse racing's Triple Crown—victories in the Kentucky
Derby, Preakness, and Belmont Stakes—was most recently won in 1948 by Citation, with Eddie Arcaro the
jockey in all three races. Arcaro rode another Triple
Crown winner, in 1941. Name the horse.

151. Rookie pitcher Floyd Giebell of the Detroit Tigers won
a game in 1940 that knocked what other major-league
baseball club out of contention for the pennant?

152. What school in Pennsylvania did the great athlete Jim
Thorpe attend?

153. Hank Majeski, Eddie Joost, Pete Suder, and Ferris Fain
(Philadelphia Athletics) combined their fielding talents
in 1949 to set what long-standing major-league record?

154. Lou Gehrig of the New York Yankees put together a
consecutive game string of 2,130 games, from June 1,
1925 to April 30, 1939, still the all-time record. Who
succeeded Gehrig as the Yankees' first baseman?

155. Name the radio broadcaster for the Joe Louis-Max

Schmeling heavyweight championship bout, held in New York City on June 22, 1938.

156. What sport did the Frankford Yellow Jackets play?

157. Johnny Vander Meer of the Cincinnati Reds is the only major-league baseball pitcher who ever threw consecutive no-hit games. The first, on June 11, 1938, was at home against Boston. The second game, on June 15, was played on the road. Where?

158. Wilcy Moore was an ace relief pitcher. He played with more than one major-league club; name the one for which he starred.

159. Joe Jacobs is credited with the expression "We was robbed!" On what occasion did he say it?

160. About a year and a half after retiring, Joe Louis attempted to regain his heavyweight boxing championship, but he lost a Sept. 27, 1950 comeback fight to whom?

161. Gertrude Ederle was not only the first woman to swim the English Channel, a feat she accomplished in the summer of 1926, but she was the first swimmer to cross the channel using a certain kind of stroke. What was it?

162. In 1920, Man o' War defeated a horse named John P. Grier in a match race that established Man o' War as the undisputed three-year-old champion. The race took place at what track in New York State?

163. What was the starring brother battery of the St. Louis Cardinals in the 1940s?

164. Who was the last major-league pitcher to legally throw a spitball?

165. Who were the touchdown-scoring football stars known as "Mr. Inside" and "Mr. Outside" at the U.S. Military Academy?

166. In July 1923, Jack Dempsey defended his heavyweight boxing title against Tom Gibbons. Instead of being held in a large city as usual, the bout took place in what small town?

167. Each of the three major-league baseball clubs in New York had an ace relief pitcher in 1947. Joe Page filled the role for the Yankees and Hugh Casey for the Dodgers. Who did the Giants have?

168. Name the opera singer who owned part of the St. Louis Browns.

169. Leo Durocher, when managing the Brooklyn Dodgers,

commented that "Nice guys finish last." Of what manager was he thinking when he said this?

170. The Associated Press conducted a poll in 1950 to determine the best football player during the first half of this century. Who was selected?

171. Who were the three regular outfielders for the 1927 New York Yankees, a club often considered the greatest baseball team of all time?

172. What contribution to sports was made by Carl E. Stotz?

173. Who was quarterback of the University of Notre Dame backfield called "The Four Horsemen"?

174. What tennis star was known as "Miss Poker Face"?

175. The New York Giants came from far behind to tie the Brooklyn Dodgers for the National League pennant in 1951. The Giants went on to win a three-game playoff series and take the pennant. The final game was won on a one-out ninth-inning home run by Bobby Thomson with two men on base. Who was pitching for the Dodgers?

176. What was the nickname of baseball pitcher Truett Sewell? Also, what was the unusual pitch he threw?

177. Baseball players whose last name is "Rhodes" or "Rhoades" usually acquire a particular nickname. Do you know what it is?

178. Who promoted the two Dempsey-Tunney heavyweight championship bouts, as well as other title fights?

179. Babe Ruth left the New York Yankees after the 1934 season. Who succeeded Ruth in right field for the Yankees?

180. In the 1929 World Series between the Philadelphia Athletics and Chicago Cubs, a veteran pitcher, supposedly over the hill, pitched the opening game for the A's and beat the Cubs 3-1, striking out a record 13 batters in the process. Name that pitcher and his catcher.

181. The St. Louis Browns won only one American League pennant, in 1944. Four pitchers started World Series games for the Browns against the St. Louis Cardinals. Name at least two of the four.

182. Johnny Paychek, Al McCoy, Gus Dorazio, and Tony Musto all fought for the heavyweight boxing championship of the world. They met the same titleholder. His name?

183. Name the owner of the Boston Red Sox who sold Babe Ruth to the New York Yankees.

184. In the third game of the 1932 World Series between the New York Yankees and Chicago Cubs, Babe Ruth pointed to the bleachers in Chicago's Wrigley Field and then hit a home run to the spot. Off what Cub pitcher did Ruth hit the homer?

185. On May 26, 1959, pitcher Harvey Haddix of the Pittsburgh Pirates set a major-league record by pitching 12 perfect innings, only to be beaten in the 13th, 1-0. Who was the winning pitcher?

186. What major league baseball club was called the "Somersets" when it began in 1901?

187. What was the name applied to Fordham University's football line composed of John Druze, Al Barbartsky, Vince Lombardi, Alex Wojciechowicz, Nat Pierce, Ed Franco, and Leo Paquin (1936-37)?

188. Roger Bannister of Great Britain was the first runner to break the four-minute mile, running a mile in 3:59.4 in 1954. Who was the first man to better Bannister's record?

189. Gene Tunney lost only 1 of 76 professional boxing matches. Who defeated him?

190. Which stable owned the great racehorse Whirlaway?

191. Name the baseball scout who discovered Lou Gehrig.

192. There has been one triple play in World Series annals, and that unassisted. In 1920, Bill Wambsganss, second baseman of the Cleveland Indians, caught a line drive, stepped on second to retire the runner who had left that base, and then tagged the runner going from first to second. Who hit the ball?

193. What did Cleveland Indian pitchers Al Smith and Jim Bagby, Jr., achieve on July 17, 1941?

194. The great athlete Jim Thorpe played major league baseball from 1913 to 1919, mostly with what club?

195. What were Babe Ruth's titles when he played part of the 1935 season with the Boston Braves?

196. What was the original name of the football franchise that became the Chicago Bears?

197. A match race was held at Washington Park in Homewood, Ill., on August 31, 1955. What two horses ran?

198. Who played first base for the St. Louis Browns when

the club almost won the American League pennant in 1922?

199. Where was the match race held on Nov. 1, 1938, between War Admiral and Seabiscuit?

200. What was the result of the first heavyweight championship fight between Joe Louis and Billy Conn, on June 18, 1941, in New York City?

201. Amos Alonzo Stagg coached football at the University of Chicago for 41 years, completing his career there in 1932. He then joined the staff of another school and coached for 14 years. The school?

202. Babe Ruth hit his 60th home run in 1927 off pitcher Tom Zachary of the Washington Senators. Who was pitching against Ruth when the Babe hit his 59th homer that year?

203. The most recent member of the Philadelphia Phillies to lead the National League in home runs was Chuck Klein, in 1933. Within five, how many homers did he hit?

204. The first divisional playoff in the National Football League was in 1933. Do you know at least one of the two teams in that playoff?

205. Jackie Robinson began his major-league baseball career in 1947 with the Brooklyn Dodgers. He had played one year of minor-league ball. With what club did he play, and what position?

206. What was the nickname of heavyweight boxer Luis Firpo?

207. Do you know the nicknames of at least two of these three major-league baseball players: Floyd Herman, Samuel Jones, and William Ewing?

208. Connie Mack retired as manager of the Philadelphia Athletics after the 1950 season, after half a century in the post. Who succeeded him?

209. Rogers Hornsby managed what major-league baseball club to its first pennant, in 1926?

210. "Little Artha" and "The Galveston Giant" were nicknames of what prize fighter?

211. Who succeeded Willie Pep twice as featherweight boxing champion?

212. Sir Thomas J. Lipton is well remembered for the tea that bears his name, but in what sport was he active?

213. What were the eight cities in the American League in 1953, before the first franchise shift?

214. After infielder Bob Dillinger left the St. Louis Browns and other major-league clubs, he played the outfield and led the Pacific Coast League in batting, in 1953. With what club?

215. What was the nickname of major-league outfielder Walter Evers?

216. Name a major-league baseball player who became a noted evangelist.

217. Where was the clubhouse located in the old Polo Grounds in New York?

218. In 1943, Count Fleet won the Kentucky Derby and the Belmont Stakes. How did he finish in the Preakness Stakes?

219. In 1921, Alvin (Bo) McMillin scored the only touchdown in a 6-0 win by what small college over Harvard University?

220. Henry Aaron first played in the All-Star Game in what year, within one?

221. What was Joe Medwick's nickname?

222. Who was the old-time Boston National League outfielder who batted .438 one year in the 1890s?

223. The Most Valuable Player in the National League in 1941 was the Brooklyn Dodgers first baseman. Identify him.

224. Name the pitcher for the Boston Red Sox and New York Yankees who won 23 straight games from the Philadelphia Athletics, from 1918 to 1923.

225. What baseball accomplishment did Mickey Mantle achieve in 1956, Joe Medwick in 1937, and Carl Yastrzemski in 1967, among others?

226. Both Tunney-Dempsey heavyweight championship bouts went the scheduled distances. How many rounds?

227. What National League baseball club won pennants in 1929, '32, '35, and '38, but lost the World Series in all four years?

228. Earl Whitehill pitched most of his career for the Detroit Tigers. He won 218 games during his major-league career, which ran from 1923 to 1939. With what club was he pitching when he won his 200th career game?

229. Name the Philadelphia Athletics catcher who didn't make an error in 117 consecutive games in 1946.

230. Who were the two 20-game-winning pitchers for the pennant-winning Cincinnati Reds in 1940? They were two of the three 20-game winners in the National League that year.

231. A shortstop for the Chicago White Sox led the American League in batting in 1943. His name?

232. Pitcher Urban Faber spent his entire 20-year major-league career with what club? What was his nickname?

233. Who hit 18 home runs for the Detroit Tigers during August 1937?

234. Longtime major-league baseball pitcher Louis (Bobo) Newsom won 211 games during his career, but what is unusual about that victory total?

235. In his first heavy-weight title defense, in 1949, Ezzard Charles knocked out what boxer?

236. In 1934, the Washington Senators traded manager-shortstop Joe Cronin to the Boston Red Sox for $250,-000 and what player?

237. Heavyweight boxing champ Bob Fitzsimmons was a native of what country?

238. Bob Feller of the Cleveland Indians was the losing pitcher in the opening game of the 1948 World Series, 1-0. Who was the winning pitcher?

239. What race horse won a record $752,550 in 1955?

240. Masterson, Pieretti, Scarborough, and Wynn were on what major-league pitching staff in the late 1940s?

241. What does 4,191 represent in the lifetime record of major-league baseball star Ty Cobb?

242. In what baseball park did Chuck Klein of the Philadelphia Phillies hit four home runs in one game in 1936?

243. Why was the Cleveland American League team once known as the Naps?

244. Lewis (Hack) Wilson had 190 of what with the Chicago Cubs in 1930?

245. Joe Walcott was listed as how old when he won the heavyweight boxing championship in 1951? Come within a year either way.

246. Who was the first player to hit a home run in the All-Star Game?

247. Who hit four home runs for the Chicago White Sox in the first game of a 1948 doubleheader?

248. Name at least one of the two men who held the heavy-

weight boxing championship between Jack Sharkey and James J. Braddock.

249. Who hit four home runs for the Brooklyn Dodgers in the 1952 World Series against the New York Yankees?

250. Stanley (Bucky) Harris managed the Washington Senators during the 1920s, again during the 1930s and early '40s, and again in the 1950s. What club did he manage in the late 1920s and early '30s, and again in 1955?

251. A sportswriter once commented about what baseball player that he was "part Indian and part first baseman"?

252. What was the Los Angeles baseball club in the Pacific Coast League called?

253. In succession, the Baseball Writers' Association picked Roy Sievers, Walt Dropo, Gil McDougald, Harry Byrd. and Harvey Kuenn for what honor?

254. In 1949, New York got a second team in the National Football League. What was its name?

255. Name the French heavyweight boxer and light-heavyweight titleholder called "The Orchid Man."

256. What charter club of the American Baseball League didn't finish last until 1952?

257. A nickname of the New York Yankees successful manager during the 1920s was "Hug." The manager was Miller Huggins. What were the nicknames of the New York Giants manager in that decade—John McGraw?

258. Two players with the New York Giants hit 51 home runs in a season. One was a right-hander, Willie Mays, in 1955. The other was a left-hander. Can you identify him?

259. What was the nickname of major-league baseball pitcher Lynwood Rowe?

260. A left-handed pitcher with the Boston Red Sox in 1916 established an American League record with nine shutouts for the season. Who was the pitcher?

261. Identify the boxing referee who worked nearly half of Joe Louis's title bouts.

262. What major-league baseball club, in its early years, was informally called the "White Elephants"?

263. Name the "me" of the baseball pitching team of "me 'n' Paul."

264. Name the pitcher who hit and almost killed Detroit Ti-

gers star catcher Mickey Cochrane in 1937. Cochrane suffered a fractured skull.

265. Against what boxer did Joe Louis make his first heavyweight title defense?

266. The leading home-run hitter in the National League in 1939 and 1940 played first base for what club?

267. Second baseman Joe Gordon was traded by the New York Yankees along with infielder Eddie Bockman to the Cleveland Indians after the 1946 season. Name the pitcher sent from Cleveland to New York in the trade.

Answers

1. Marty Marion.
2. Dempsey knocked out Jess Willard in the third round. (The fight was held in Toledo, Ohio.)
3. A total of 113:54 in 1920 and 59 in '21.
4. Madison Square Garden.
5. Ty Cobb.
6. Harold (Red) Grange.
7. Bill Terry, in 1932.
8. Eighth.
9. Pitcher. He won 194 regular season games.
10. Boxing. He was middleweight champ in the early part of this century. Ring name: Stanley Ketchel.
11. That of Grantland Rice.
12. Cleveland Indians. The club used League Park and Municipal Stadium.
13. Allie Reynolds.
14. 1923.
15. Alan Ameche scored a touchdown.
16. Glasses.
17. Ezzard Charles, who carried Marciano the full 15 rounds before losing a decision to him in 1954. In another meeting three months later, Charles lost to Marciano by an eighth-round KO.
18. Yankee Stadium, New York. It opened in 1923 and was made possible to a great extent by the popularity and drawing power of Babe Ruth.
19. Lou Groza of the Cleveland Browns, in games from 1950 to 1955, and 1957, '64, and '65.
20. Alexander.
21. Essegian hit two pinch-hit home runs, the only player ever to do this in a World Series.
22. 14.
23. Philadelphia Athletics (1927–28).
24. 1936.
25. Robert Moses (Lefty) Grove.
26. Dayton.

27. Otto Graham.
28. Rogers Hornsby.
29. Herb Pennock of the Boston Red Sox.
30. .424. (He played in 143 games.)
31. Equipoise.
32. Washington Senators (American League). He batted .379.
33. Paul was "Big Poison" and Lloyd was "Little Poison."
34. Spitball.
35. Pete Rademacher. Patterson scored a sixth-round knockout.
36. Belmont Park, Jamaica, Aqueduct, and Saratoga.
37. Paul Hornung.
38. The team won 110 games for a winning percentage of .714.
39. Dominic, Joseph, and Vincent.
40. Primo Carnera.
41. Pennsylvania (Aug. 31, 1895). Latrobe beat Jeannette, 12–0.
42. Calumet Farm.
43. "The Pittsburgh Kid."
44. He hit into a triple play and a double play in successive times at bat.
45. Mickey Walker; welterweight and middleweight.
46. Dark Star defeated Native Dancer by a head in the 1953 Kentucky Derby.
47. He was not in good health and that year was fined $5,000 for "misconduct off the ball field."
48. The Giants were wearing basketball shoes. They scored 27 points in the final quarter to overcome a 13–3 Chicago lead.
49. Green Bay Packers and Kansas City Chiefs. Green Bay won, 35–10.
50. Swaps; Hollywood Park, Calif.
51. Tommy Burns.
52. He made an unassisted triple play.
53. Otto Graham.
54. Bob Feller; Cleveland Indians.
55. The first Joe Louis–Billy Conn fight. Louis won a knockout in the closing seconds of the 13th round.
56. Bucko Kilroy.
57. Boston Red Sox.
58. Lawrin in 1938; Whirlaway in '41; Hoop, Jr., in '45; Citation in '48; and Hill Gail in '52.
59. Chicago Bears 73, Washington Redskins 0, in 1940. The Bears scored 11 touchdowns.
60. Elroy Face.
61. Sugar Ramos won the featherweight championship.
62. Grover Cleveland Alexander and Christy Mathewson.
63. .625 (10 hits in 16 times at bat).
64. George Sisler of the St. Louis Browns, who hit .407 in 1920 and .420 in 1922.
65. Paul (Dizzy) Trout.
66. He had only one leg. He played in only one league game, for the Washington Senators in 1945.
67. Floyd Patterson and Ingemar Johansson, who met for the heavyweight championship in June 1959, June 1960, and March 1961.

68. 300.
69. Baker hit two of the three Series home runs.
70. Bill Terry (New York Giants), who batted .401 in 1930.
71. "Spud."
72. Henry Armstrong—welter, light, and featherweight. He won all three titles in less than ten months.
73. Blue Jays.
74. Fourth of eight clubs.
75. Grover Cleveland Alexander. Johnson pitched 113 shutouts; Alexander, 90.
76. Joe Walcott and Joe Louis, respectively. Louis won a 15-round decision to retain his heavyweight championship.
77. Russell. The years were 1910 and '11.
78. His regular season wins and losses as a pitcher.
79. James J. Braddock.
80. Yogi Berra, who played in 75 games in 14 Series.
81. Halfback Gale Sayers.
82. Joe DiMaggio, with 46 homers in 1937.
83. The game went 26 innings with Leon Cadore pitching for Brooklyn and Joe Oeschger for Boston.
84. John (Pepper) Martin.
85. Lightweight.
86. Detroit Tigers (1930–46).
87. Harry Brecheen.
88. New York Yankees (1960). The Pittsburgh Pirates won the Series in seven games.
89. Arthur Donovan.
90. For the Boston Braves against the Pittsburgh Pirates.
91. Joe Hauser, who belted 27 home runs in 1924.
92. The Yankees finished third in 1940, two games behind pennant-winning Detroit and one game behind second-place Cleveland.
93. John L. Sullivan.
94. Elmer F. Layden (1941–46).
95. Dale Mitchell; called out on strikes.
96. None.
97. Zev in 1923, Flying Ebony in 1925, and Gallant Fox in 1930.
98. Sal Maglie.
99. Washington Senators.
100. Tris Speaker, who hit 793 doubles. Stan Musial is second with 725.
101. Dizzy Dean.
102. Joey Maxim. Moore won all three fights by 15-round decisions.
103. Green Bay and Boston. The Redskins moved to Washington the following year.
104. Rogers Hornsby, who batted .358 in 23 seasons.
105. He pitched the longest Series game, 14 innings, and won it 2–1.
106. Ezzard Charles.
107. Twenty.
108. Citation.
109. The team won the 1914 Series four games to none against a great Philadelphia Athletics club.
110. Roy Cullenbine.

111. Bob Feller.
112. He batted .313.
113. Joe Louis vs. Abe Simon, in Detroit on March 21, 1941. Louis KO'd Simon in 13 rounds.
114. Brooklyn Dodgers.
115. Mickey Cochrane.
116. Miniature ("Tom Thumb") golf.
117. He was a pitcher; with Newark of the International League he won 23 games while losing only 4, in 1941.
118. Max West.
119. Wes Ferrell (Cleveland Indians).
120. Tony Cuccinello, who batted .308. He retired as an active player after the 1945 season.
121. "Flash."
122. Wesleyan and Yale, in 1906. The first forward pass was thrown by a Wesleyan player.
123. Third base, with most of his play there before he became a regular pitcher. He played second base and elsewhere a few times.
124. 76.
125. Black and yellow.
126. The game took place indoors, in the Chicago Stadium.
127. Columbia.
128. He won on a foul in the fourth round.
129. Red Faber (23 victories), Claude Williams (22), Dick Kerr (21), and Eddie Cicotte (21).
130. Sam Riddle.
131. Eddie Collins.
132. Bobby Jones.
133. He hit three home runs in one game.
134. Archie Moore. Marciano won a ninth-round KO.
135. Carl Hubbell of the New York Giants, in 1936 and 1937.
136. Boston Red Sox.
137. Second baseman Eddie Stanky.
138. Lou Gehrig.
139. Joe Walcott; Joey Maxim.
140. Dave (Boo) Ferriss.
141. Count Fleet (1943); One Count (1952).
142. The Cubs traded outfielder Max Flack to the Cardinals for outfielder Clifton Heathcote. The trade was made between games of a morning-afternoon doubleheader, so that both players played for two teams in one day.
143. "Hub," "King Carl," and "Meal Ticket."
144. The referee had mistakenly allowed Cornell a fifth down on which that team scored a touchdown.
145. St. Louis Cardinals. In order, those were nicknames for James Collins, Frank Frisch, John Martin, and Leo Durocher.
146. His own. Ruth hit 59 homers for the New York Yankees in 1921.
147. Cleveland Indians.
148. Dr. James A. Naismith, an instructor at the International YMCA Training School, Springfield, Mass. (1891).
149. .367.

150. Whirlaway. Both Citation and Whirlaway were owned by Warren Wright.
151. Giebell beat the Cleveland Indians, 2–0. The game was his third and final major-league pitching victory.
152. Carlisle Indian School, Carlisle, Pa.
153. 217 double plays in a season.
154. Ellsworth (Babe) Dahlgren.
155. Clem McCarthy.
156. Football. This National Football League franchise was transferred to a Philadelphia (Eagles) group in 1933.
157. Ebbets Field, Brooklyn.
158. New York Yankees.
159. Jacobs was manager of heavyweight boxer Max Schmeling when Schmeling lost a decision and the championship in June 1932 to Jack Sharkey. Jacobs shouted "We was robbed!" into a radio microphone on a coast-to-coast broadcast.
160. Ezzard Charles, who won a 15-round decision.
161. Crawl.
162. Aqueduct.
163. Pitcher Morton and catcher Walker Cooper.
164. Burleigh Grimes, who ended his major-league career in 1934.
165. Fullback Felix (Doc) Blanchard and halfback Glenn Davis. The two starred on undefeated Army teams in 1944, '45, and '46.
166. Shelby, Mont.
167. Ken Trinkle.
168. Helen Traubel.
169. Mel Ott, manager of the last-place New York Giants.
170. Jim Thorpe. Harold (Red) Grange was second and Bronko Nagurski a distant third.
171. Bob Meusel, left field; Earle Combs, center field; and Babe Ruth, right field.
172. He founded Little League Baseball in the late 1930s.
173. Harry Stuhldreher. (The others were Jimmy Crowley, left halfback; Don Miller, right halfback; and Elmer Layden, fullback.)
174. Helen Wills.
175. Ralph Branca.
176. His nickname was "Rip." He threw a slow "blooper" pitch that formed an arc perhaps 30 feet high.
177. "Dusty."
178. Tex Rickard.
179. George Selkirk.
180. Howard Ehmke; Mickey Cochrane.
181. Denny Galehouse, Nelson Potter, Jack Kramer, and Sig Jakucki.
182. Joe Louis.
183. Harry Frazee. He was a theatrical producer, and he sold Ruth and other players to raise money for a new musical comedy—"No, No, Nanette."
184. Charlie Root.
185. Lew Burdette of the Milwaukee Braves.
186. Boston Red Sox. Charles Somers was their first owner.
187. "Seven Blocks of Granite."

188. John Landy of Australia, also in 1954. He ran the mile in 3:58.
189. Harry Greb, in 15 rounds in 1922. Greb won the light-heavyweight title from Tunney.
190. Calumet Farm.
191. Paul Krichell of the New York Yankees, at Columbia University.
192. Clarence Mitchell, Brooklyn Dodgers pitcher.
193. They stopped Joe DiMaggio from extending his record 56-game hitting streak.
194. New York Giants.
195. Vice-president and assistant manager.
196. Staley Athletic Club, Decatur, Ill. The team was transferred to Chicago and renamed the Bears in January 1922.
197. Swaps and Nashua. Nashua won.
198. George Sisler.
199. Pimlico.
200. Louis knocked out Conn in 13 rounds.
201. College of the Pacific, Stockton, Calif.
202. Rookie pitcher Paul Hopkins of the Senators.
203. 28.
204. Chicago Bears and New York Giants. The Bears won, 23–21.
205. He played first base for Montreal (International League) in 1946, and won the league's batting championship.
206. "Wild Bull of the Pampas."
207. "Babe"; "Sad Sam"; "Buck."
208. Jimmy Dykes.
209. St. Louis Cardinals.
210. Jack Johnson, heavyweight champion of the world from 1908 to 1915.
211. Sandy Saddler.
212. Yachting. He competed for the America's Cup five times.
213. Boston, New York, Philadelphia, Washington, Cleveland, Chicago, Detroit, and St. Louis,.
214. Sacramento. In 171 games he batted .366.
215. "Hoot."
216. Billy Sunday.
217. In straightaway center field, more than 480 feet from home plate.
218. Also first.
219. Centre College, Danville, Ky.
220. 1955. Aaron played in the All-Star Game every year since, but didn't hit his first All-Star homer unil 1971.
221. "Ducky Wucky."
222. Hugh Duffy (1894).
223. Dolph Camilli.
224. Carl Mays.
225. They won baseball's "triple crown," which means each led his league in batting average, home runs, and runs batted in.
226. 10 rounds each. Tunney won by decisions.
227. Chicago Cubs.
228. Cleveland Indians, (1937). He defeated the Washington Senators, the club he pitched for from 1933 through 1936.
229. Warren (Buddy) Rosar.
230. Bucky Walters and Paul Derringer.

231. Luke Appling, who batted .328 that year. He also led in 1936 with .388.
232. Chicago White Sox; "Red." (He won 253 games, losing 211.)
233. Rudy York.
234. It's less than his loss total of 222 games. His winning percentage of .487 is the lowest of pitchers who have won at least 200 games.
235. Gus Lesnevich
236. Shortstop Lyn Lary.
237. England.
238. Johnny Sain.
239. Nashua.
240. Washington Senators.
241. The number of hits during his regular season major-league career, tops for any player.
242. Forbes Field, Pittsburgh.
243. Because the team's manager at the time was Napoleon (Nap) Lajoie.
244. Runs batted in, still the major-league record for one season.
245. 37.
246. Babe Ruth, in the third inning of the first All-Star Game (1933).
247. Outfielder Pat Seerey.
248. Primo Carnera and Max Baer (1933 and 1934).
249. Edwin (Duke) Snider.
250. Detroit Tigers. He also managed the Boston Red Sox, Philadelphia Phillies, and New York Yankees.
251. Rudy York.
252. Angels.
253. American League rookie of the year (1949-53).
254. Bulldogs.
255. Georges Carpentier.
256. Detroit Tigers.
257. "Mac" or "Muggsy."
258. Johnny Mize (1947).
259. "Schoolboy."
260. Babe Ruth.
261. Arthur Donovan.
262. Philadelphia Athletics.
263. Dizzy Dean. Paul was his brother Paul Dean.
264. Irving (Bump) Hadley (New York Yankees).
265. Tommy Farr, (Aug. 30, 1937). Louis had won the title from James J. Braddock in June 1937.
266. St. Louis Cardinals, (Johnny Mize).
267. Allie Reynolds.

POLITICS

1. Who originated the symbols of the Democratic and Republican parties—the donkey and the elephant?
2. Alexander Hamilton, ex-Secretary of the Treasury, was killed in a duel in 1804 at Weehawken, N.J. Who was his opponent?
3. Name the first woman elected to Congress.
4. The first woman governor was Nellie Tayloe Ross. She was elected in what state?
5. What was the name of the political machine controlled by "Boss" William M. Tweed?
6. Who was Chief Justice of the U.S. when the Supreme Court Justices were called the "nine old men"?
7. Who was the first U.S. Secretary of State?
8. Andrew W. Mellon served as Secretary of the Treasury under what three Republican Presidents?
9. Which Congressman, first serving in the House of Representatives in 1873, was elected Speaker in 1903 and continued in that office to 1911?
10. In what year did the New Deal begin?
11. "Sir, I would rather be right than be President" is a remark made more than a century ago by what American statesman?
12. Who was Chief Justice of the U.S. when a majority of the Supreme Court declared in the Dred Scott case that Congress did not have power to exclude slavery from the territories?
13. The Joseph Grundy political machine was operative in what state?
14. What was the Cabinet post held by Henry C. Wallace and his son Henry A. Wallace?
15. What politician did Alice Roosevelt Longworth compare in looks to the bridegroom on a wedding cake?
16. Name the woman who was elected governor of Texas in 1925.

Answers

1. Political cartoonist Thomas Nast (1840–1902). He also originated the modern conception of Santa Claus.
2. Aaron Burr, Vice-President of the U.S. Hamilton fired in the air but Burr didn't.
3. Miss Jeanette Rankin of Montana. She served in Congress from 1917 to 1919 and again from 1941 to 1943.
4. Wyoming (1924).
5. Tammany Hall (in New York City).
6. Charles Evans Hughes.
7. Thomas Jefferson (1790–93).
8. Harding, Coolidge, Hoover (1921–32).
9. Joe Cannon.
10. 1933, when Franklin D. Roosevelt became President.
11. Henry Clay (in 1850).
12. Roger B. Taney.
13. Pennsylvania.
14. Secretary of Agriculture (Henry C., 1921–24; Henry A., 1933–40).
15. Thomas E. Dewey.
16. Miriam (Ma) Ferguson.

ADVERTISING

1. What make of piano was promoted in the "They laughed when I sat down to play" advertisement?
2. Years ago, the name of sodium alkyl sulfate in Pepsodent toothpaste was changed to what single word?
3. What electrical appliance was advertised as economical because it had a "Meter Miser"?
4. According to the commercial, what cigarette's "green" went to war?
5. What brand of soap is used for "the skin you love to touch"?
6. Fill in the blank in the old ad slogan, "Time to Retire? Buy ———."
7. What brand of toothpaste, once a big seller, has been advertised as "good for tender gums"?
8. "It's moisturized" was a slogan for what brand of cigarette?
9. What airplane has been known as the "Workhorse of the Skies"?
10. "Just enough Turkish" promoted what cigarette?
11. One of the most successful ad slogans of all time was "Reach for a ——— instead of a sweet." Fill in the brand name.
12. Name the food product advertised to "make good foods taste better."
13. What soft drink promised "zip in every sip"?
14. What brand of cigarette was advertised by two dancing girls inside cigarette packs?
15. What company advertised its products as serving from "head to foot, cellar to attic"?
16. What brand of soap used this ad line: "Soap from trees—nature's gift to beauty"?
17. Can you identify the so-called health product, invented by Louisiana State Senator Dudley J. LeBlanc, that was a big seller more than two decades ago?
18. "Save with safety, shave with safety" was a slogan for what make of razor blades?

19. What make of washing machine has been advertised, "As gentle as human hands"?

20. What pen was advertised saying that it "makes its mark around the world"?

21. According to the old ad slogan, "If it's lovely to wear it's worth —————— —————— care." Fill in the blanks.

22. "The famous skin softener" was a slogan used for what product?

23. "Even your best friends won't tell you" was a lead line in advertisements for what product?

24. Name the cereal promoted as "the great American family cereal."

25. What tobacco company included among its early cigarette brands "Crimps," "Morey's Best," "Tent," and "Fatima"?

26. What company used the slogan "Years ahead in the science of flight"?

27. Which airline promoted itself as "the main line airway"?

28. What brand of toothpaste had a red-colored tube "for teeth easy to bryten" and a blue-colored tube "for teeth hard to bryten"?

29. "Delicious, nutritious, makes you feel ambitious" came from the advertising slogan for what food product?

30. What business was William Wrigley in before chewing gum?

31. Fill in the missing word, which is the name of a product: "When the telephone has a bad breath, that's the time to take a —————."

32. "In one hour your top men will be 220 miles ahead" is an ad that promoted what?

33. What soft-drink company once had the slogan, "Those who think are proud to drink . . ."?

34. "We tried 130 times before we perfected a shaving cream like this" was part of an advertisement for what brand of shaving cream?

35. An early 20th-century ad for what soap began: "The sweetest thing on earth is the face of a little child. Its skin is exquisitely delicate, like the bloom of a ripe peach. Imagine washing a peach with colored and perfumed soap"?

36. The slogan "Brewery goodness sealed right in" promoted what beer?

37. There were four Jell-O flavors around the turn of the century. Three of them were orange, lemon and strawberry. What was the other?

38. "Often a bridesmaid, never a bride" promoted what product?

39. What was the name used by Elsa Miranda when she sang a banana commercial for the United Fruit Company?

40. The slogan "162 brushings in the 40-cent tube" was used for what brand of toothpaste?

41. "Are you true to your type?" is a slogan that promoted what item of men's clothing?

42. Name the brand of razor blade which advertised that it "has the edge five ways."

43. Fill in the name of the washing product that completes this short advertising slogan: "Trust _____ _____."

44. "Wheat Berries" and "Puffed Berries" were earlier names for what products of the Quaker Oats Company?

45. In Pepsodent toothpaste commercials, who was the woman who neglected using "Irium"?

46. What brand of cigar was mentioned in this radio commercial: "All the world is serene in that moment supreme—when you're smoking a _____ cigar"?

47. What is the trade name that was originated in 1876 by Bradley, Voorhees, and Day?

48. "First in Favor and Flavor" has been an on-the-package advertising slogan of a company long noted for its lack of advertising. The firm?

49. "Keep that schoolgirl complexion" was an ad slogan for what soap?

50. Name the product that advertised a "14-day beauty plan."

51. What was the first cigarette to use advertisements featuring women?

52. To what does the slogan "The instrument of the immortals" refer?

53. What product made the word "halitosis" well known?

54. "Good for you and good to you" is an old slogan for what product?

55. Fill in the word in this old advertising slogan: "If it's safe in water, it's safe in _____."

56. What is the product that the manufacturer said "hasn't scratched yet"?

57. "They work while you sleep" was an ad slogan for what product?

58. For what product was the slogan "Eventually, why not now?" used?

59. "Like old friends, they wear well" was an advertising slogan for what kind of wearing apparel?

60. "Ginger ale with piquant personality" was a line used by what soft-drink company?

61. Johnny Roventini is the Johnny of Philip Morris fame, best known for his "Call for Phil-lip Mor-ress." What was his occupation before he was hired by Philip Morris in 1933?

62. One of radio's first singing commercials had these lines: "No brush, no lather, no rub-in / Wet your razor, then begin . . ." What was the product?

63. "Always milder, Better tasting, Cooler smoking" was in the ad for a brand of cigarettes. Name the brand.

64. In advertising, identify Nipper, a black-and-white fox terrier.

65. Where did Elsie the Cow make her first public appearance?

66. Baron George Wrangell for years has been part of a leading advertising symbol. In what way?

67. What is the laundry product whose maker once claimed it could do everything?

68. Fill in the brand name for the following old ad slogan: "Take hospital-tested ———— and feel good again!"

69. What product was described in ads as "so round, so firm, so fully packed, so free and easy on the draw"?

70. Name the oil company represented by the trade name Secony.

71. What product was advertised by the slogan "Children cry for it?"

72. What was "at your grocer's, at your fingertips"?

73. Phoebe Snow rode the Road of Anthracite in advertisements for what railroad?

74. What brand of soap advertised that it contained "no phoolium"?

75. What was the shaving product that was advertised by series of rhyming roadside signs?

76. "They're milder; they taste better" was a slogan for what brand of cigarette?

77. In this R. T. French ad, fill in the blank with a pet: "Your ———— may be overfed, yet undernourished."

78. "World's best-tasting breakfast food" promoted what product?

79. What brand of cat food was advertised as "his master's choice"?

80. "The global high sign" was a slogan used by what product?

81. What company made the Radiola Super-Heterodyne radio?

Answers

1. Steinway.
2. "Irium."
3. Frigidaire brand refrigerator.
4. Lucky Strike's. This referred to a wartime change in the smoke's packaging.
5. Woodbury.
6. Fisk.
7. Ipana.
8. Raleigh.
9. Douglas DC-3.
10. Fatima.
11. Lucky (for Lucky Strike).
12. Heinz tomato catsup.
13. Spur.
14. Old Gold.
15. Fuller Brush Company.
16. Palmolive.
17. Hadacol.
18. Gem.
19. Easy.
20. Waterman.
21. "Ivory Flakes."
22. Campana Balm.
23. Listerine.
24. Cream of Wheat.
25. Liggett & Myers.
26. Lockheed.
27. United.
28. Iodent.
29. Quaker Oats.
30. Baking powder.
31. Cascaret.
32. Cessna aircraft.

33. Hires.
34. Palmolive.
35. Ivory.
36. Pabst.
37. Raspberry.
38. Listerine.
39. "Chiquita Banana."
40. Listerine.
41. Hats (Stetson).
42. Pal.
43. Silver Dust.
44. Puffed Wheat and Puffed Rice.
45. Miriam.
46. Blackstone.
47. "BVD."
48. Hershey Chocolate Corporation (now Hershey Foods Corporation).
49. Palmolive.
50. Palmolive soap.
51. Chesterfield (1926).
52. Steinway pianos.
53. Listerine.
54. Ry-Krisp.
55. Lux.
56. Bon Ami cleanser.
57. Cascarets.
58. Gold Medal flour.
59. Gloves (made by Louis Meyers & Son).
60. Cliquot Club.
61. Bellboy.
62. Barbasol.
63. Chesterfield.
64. The model for "His Master's Voice"—a trademark of RCA Victor.
65. The Borden Company first displayed Elsie, a purebred Jersey, at the New York World's Fair of 1939.
66. He is the man in the Hathaway shirt, with a patch over his right eye.
67. Duz. The slogan: "Duz does everything."
68. Pepto-Bismol.
69. Lucky Strike cigarettes.
70. Standard Oil Corporation of New York.
71. Fletcher's Castoria.
72. Campbell's soups.
73. Lackawanna (Delaware, Lackawanna, & Western).
74. Strykers.
75. Burma Shave.
76. Chesterfield.
77. Canary.
78. Quaker Oats.
79. Calo.
80. Coca-Cola.
81. Radio Corporation of America (RCA).

MUSICALS

1. In the early 1930s, Ed Wynn starred in the musical "The Laugh Parade." Why was the show closed every Tuesday?
2. Who "stopped the show" with her rendition of "My Heart Belongs to Daddy" in the 1938 musical "Leave It to Me"?
3. Name the musical introduced by the Theatre Guild in 1945 which included in its score "If I Loved You," by Rodgers and Hammerstein.
4. What is the name of the carnival barker in the stage musical and movie "Carousel"?
5. "Bewitched, Bothered, and Bewildered" was in the score of what musical?
6. The song "Oh, How I Hate to Get Up in the Morning," by Irving Berlin, recalls the World War I era. The musical in which it was introduced ran for only 32 performances. Identify it.
7. Who sang "Old Man River" in the original production of "Show Boat"? He was a baritone.
8. "Rhapsody in Blue," by George Gershwin, was introduced to the public at Aeolian Hall in New York in February 1924. Who led the orchestra that evening?
9. The 1924 musical comedy "Lady, Be Good!" featured Fred and Adele Astaire. Who wrote the music for it?
10. Betty Compton, Adele and Fred Astaire, William Kent, Victor Moore, and Allen Kearns starred in what 1927 stage musical?
11. Who introduced "I Got Rhythm" in the 1930 stage hit "Girl Crazy"?
12. In what musical was "All the Things You Are" introduced?
13. "Only Make Believe" was introduced in what stage musical?
14. In what 1928 musical did Helen Kane sing "I Wanna Be Loved by You"?
15. "Taking A Chance on Love" is from what 1940 musical?

16. Irving Berlin wrote the music for a show in which all the actors were men in military service. The hit song was "I Left My Heart at the Stage Door Canteen." Name the show.

17. "Without a Song" is from what musical?

18. Name the dance team that starred in the 1922 musical "For Goodness' Sake."

19. "I Whistle a Happy Tune" is from what musical?

20. The song "Stranger in Paradise" is from what early 1950s musical?

21. What bird was asked the question, "Why do you sit, singing 'Willow, titwillow, titwillow' "?

22. George and Ira Gershwin's "Fascinating Rhythm" appeared in what 1924 musical starring Fred and Adele Astaire?

23. Who wrote the operetta "Naughty Marietta"?

Answers

1. So that Wynn could broadcast his "Texaco Fire Chief" radio program.
2. Mary Martin.
3. "Carousel."
4. Billy Bigelow.
5. "Pal Joey."
6. "Yip, Yip, Yaphank" (opened September 1918).
7. Jules Bledsoe.
8. Paul Whiteman.
9. George Gershwin.
10. "Funny Face."
11. Ethel Merman.
12. "Very Warm for May" (1939), with music by Jerome Kern and Oscar Hammerstein II.
13. "Show Boat."
14. "Good Boy."
15. "Cabin in the Sky."
16. "This Is the Army."
17. "Great Day."
18. Fred and Adele Astaire.
19. "The King and I."
20. "Kismet."
21. The dickeybird or tomtit in Gilbert and Sullivan's "Mikado."
22. "Lady, Be Good!"
23. Victor Herbert.

POETRY

1. In "The Shooting of Dan McGrew," by Robert W. Service, a stranger shoots Dan McGrew. What kind of shirt is the stranger wearing?

2. In Edward Lear's "The Owl and the Pussy-Cat," what does Pussy call the Owl?

3. In "Casey at the Bat," who precedes Casey in Mudville's batting order?

4. What line precedes "Are losing theirs and blaming it on you"?

5. What is the name of the lady mentioned in "The Shooting of Dan McGrew"?

6. "For purple mountain majesties / Above the fruited plain" are lines of what patriotic song-poem?

7. "When I was sick and lay a-bed / I had two pillows at my head / And all my toys beside me lay / To keep me happy all the day" are the lines of the opening stanza of which Robert Louis Stevenson poem?

8. What church is mentioned in "Paul Revere's Ride," by Henry Wadsworth Longfellow?

9. To whom is Little Boy Blue talking when he says, "Now, don't you go till I come," in the poem by Eugene Field?

10. "When true hearts lie withered / And fond ones are flown / Oh! who would inhabit / This bleak world alone" are the last lines of what poem by Thomas Moore?

11. "A fool there was, and she lowered her pride / (Even as you and I)" are the first two lines of a poem that is the answer to another poem. Name it and its author.

12. The four-line verse "Always Finish" is by an anonymous author. It begins: "If a task is once begun / Never leave it till it's done." Do you know the rest?

13. Jane Taylor wrote "Twinkle, Twinkle, Little Star," which begins: "Twinkle, twinkle, little star / How I wonder what you are." Can you recall the remaining two lines of the first stanza?

14. "Tweedledum and Tweedledee agreed to have a battle / For Tweedledum said Tweedledee had spoiled his nice

new rattle" are lines from Lewis Carroll's "Through the Looking Glass." What are the next two lines?

15. Who planted the tree in George Pope Morris's "Woodman, Spare That Tree"?

16. "'Tis the set of the sails / And not the gales / Which tells us the way to go" are lines from "The Winds of Fate." The author?

17. "Little drops of water / Little grains of sand / Make the mighty ocean / And the pleasant land" are the first four lines of Julia Fletcher's "Little Things." What are the four remaining lines?

18. "And each forgets, as he strips and runs / With a brilliant, fitful pace" are two lines from "The Men That Don't Fit In," by Robert W. Service. What are the next two lines?

19. In "Lochinvar," by Sir Walter Scott, what was to take place in the Netherby hall?

20. "Wynken, Blynken, and Nod one night / Sailed off in a wooden shoe" is the beginning of "A Dutch Lullaby," by Eugene Field. What does the poet say that Wynken, Blynken, and Nod really are?

21. In James Russell Lowell's "Yussouf," who came one night to Yussouf's tent?

22. Who is Basil Underwood, mentioned in a poem by Rosa Hartwick Thorpe?

23. Fill in the missing name in this stanza of poetry: "We called him ————. He was just a cur / But twice on the Western Line / That little old bunch of faithful fur / Had offered his life for mine."

24. How long had grandfather's clock stood on the floor, in "Grandfather's Clock," by Henry Clay Work?

25. "A wise old owl lived in an oak / The more he saw the less he spoke" are the first two lines of Edward Hersey Richards's "A Wise Old Owl." What are the remaining lines?

26. "Why may not I, as well as these / Grow lovely, growing old" are the last two lines of Karle Wilson Baker's "Let Me Grow Lovely." What are "these"?

27. "Father calls me William, sister calls me Will / Mother calls me Willie, but the fellers call me Bill" are lines from the first stanza of a poem by Eugene Field. Its title?

28. What are the first two lines of the poem that ends: "A

mind at peace with all below / A heart whose love is innocent!"?

29. The first three lines of a poem by Edward Harrigan are: "Preserve that old kettle, so blackened and worn / It belonged to my father before I was born / It hung in a corner beyant on a nail . . ." For what was the kettle used?

30. Fill in the missing words in these lines of "The Human Touch," by Spencer Michael Free: " 'Tis the human touch in this world that counts / The touch of your hand and mine / Which means far more to the fainting heart / Than ——— and ——— and ———."

31. What are the last four lines of Rudyard Kipling's "If—"?

32. Who are the "old ones" the poet refers to when he says: "The old ones, with their wistful, fading eyes / They who desire no further paradise . . . Each word and gesture; they who lie and wait / To welcome us— with no rebuke if late"?

33. Name the author of the poem that has these lines: "They're making my money diminish / I'm sick of the taste of champagne / Thank God! when I'm skinned to a finish / I'll pike to the Yukon again"?

34. The title of a poem by Sir Walter Scott is the same as the word omitted from the following, first two, lines: "Oh, young ——— is come out of the West / Through all the wild Border his steed was the best."

35. What is the name of the British man-of-war mentioned in "Paul Revere's Ride"?

36. "The Man on the Flying Trapeze" begins: "Once I was happy, but now I'm forlorn." What is the following line?

37. In Lewis Carroll's "The Walrus and the Carpenter," why is it odd that the sun shines on the sea?

38. What line is repeated in every stanza of Rudyard Kipling's poem "Boots"?

39. According to James Russell Lowell's "The First Snow-fall," "Every pine and fir and hemlock" wore what?

40. In "Frankie and Johnny," where did Frankie buy a gun?

41. What was the score against the Mudville team when Mighty Casey struck out, in "Casey at the Bat"?

42. In the poem "Fable" by Ralph Waldo Emerson, the

squirrel says to the mountain, "If I cannot carry forests on my back, neither can you" do what?

43. What is Alph, in "Kubla Khan," by Samuel Taylor Coleridge?

44. Do you know the first two lines of the poem "America, the Beautiful"?

45. "Twas brillig, and the slithy toves / Did gyre and gimble in the wabe" are the first two lines of what poem by Lewis Carroll?

46. The story described in "The Face upon the Floor" took place in what season of the year?

47. What does Wordsworth describe as "fluttering and dancin the breeze" and "tossing their heads in sprightly dance"?

48. In what poem by John Masefield is the wind likened to a "whetted knife"?

49. "Wealth I seek not, hope nor love / Nor a friend to know me / All I seek, the heaven above / And the road below me" are lines from "The Vagabond." Who wrote it?

50. What is the name of the child in "The First Snowfall," by James Russell Lowell? She asks, "Father, who makes it snow?"

51. According to Christina Georgina Rossetti's "The Wind," how does one know when the wind passes by?

52. "O, the Raggedy Man he works fer Pa / An' he's the goodest man ever you saw!" is from a poem by James Whitcomb Riley. What is its title?

53. "A fool there was and he made his prayer" is the opening line of Rudyard Kipling's "The Vampire." To whom did the fool make his prayer?

54. Quote the line of poetry that immediately precedes "Whether 'tis nobler in the mind to suffer."

55. "If you can make one heap of all your winnings / And risk it on one turn of pitch-and-toss" are two lines from Rudyard Kipling's "If—." What are the next two lines?

56. What became of the gingham dog and the calico cat in Eugene Field's poem "The Duel"?

57. In Eugene Field's "A Dutch Lullaby," what was used as a boat by Wynken, Blynken, and Nod?

58. "There are two kinds of people on earth today" wrote Ella Wheeler Wilcox in one of her poems. Do you know the kinds she meant?

59. "There is so much good in the worst of us / And so much bad in the best of us" are the first two lines of "Charity." What are the remaining two lines?

60. In "The Face upon the Floor," by H. Antoine D'Arcy, the vagabond reveals to the crowd in Joe's barroom that he has once been in love with a beautiful woman. What is her name?

61. The moonlight is mentioned throughout Alfred Noyes's "The Highwayman." How is the moon described?

62. Following are two lines of a poem by Edgar Smith: "You may tempt the upper classes / With your villainous demi-tasses." What is the next line?

63. Where is the baseball game being played in Ernest L. Thayer's "Casey at the Bat"?

64. Three children are mentioned in Longfellow's "The Children's Hour." Two of them are Alice and Allegra. Who is the third? What is the color of her hair?

65. In James Whitcomb Riley's "Little Orphant Annie," the children are sitting around the kitchen fire listening to Annie. What are they listening to her tell about?

66. In the four-line poem "A Boston Toast," by John C. Bossidy, what two family names are mentioned?

67. "If you can talk with crowds and keep your virtue" is a line from Rudyard Kipling's poem "If—." What is the line that follows?

68. "Days of Birth" begins, "Monday's child is fair of face," and it goes on to say something about children born on every day of the week. What about a child "born on the Sabbath day"?

69. What does John Greenleaf Whittier call shoes in "The Barefoot Boy"?

70. What is the title of the poem in which Basil Underwood, Bessie, and Cromwell are mentioned? It was written by Rosa Hartwick Thorpe.

71. In "Abou Ben Adhem," by Leigh Hunt, what does Abou see when he awakes one night from a deep dream of peace?

72. "I never saw a purple cow / I never hope to see one" are the first two lines of "The Purple Cow," by Gelett Burgess. There are two more lines. What are they?

73. Who said: "The time has come—to talk of many things / Of shoes—and ships—and sealing wax—Of cabbages—and kings"?

POETRY

74. What is the title of the poem by Robert W. Service in which the Malamute saloon is mentioned?

75. "A bag of tools, a shapeless mass, a book of rules" are given to each of us, according to R. L. Sharpe in "A Bag of Tools." What is to be made with them?

76. In "The Three Fishers," by Charles Kingsley, "Three fishers went sailing away to the west." Where were their wives?

77. In what month do the events in John Greenleaf Whittier's "Barbara Frietchie" occur?

78. Who is called "Little Prig" in a poem by Ralph Waldo Emerson?

79. A dog bites a man and the dog dies in Oliver Goldsmith's "Elegy on the Death of a Mad Dog." What is the community where the incident occurs?

80. In "A Wise Old Owl," by Edward Hersey Richards, where does the owl live?

81. "These are the days when skies put on / The old, old sophistries of June" are lines from a poem by what woman?

82. According to "Days of Birth," "Tuesday's child is full of grace." What about children born on Wednesday and Thursday?

83. What is the title of the poem by Eugene Field in which Wynken, Blynken, and Nod sail off in a wooden shoe?

84. "There are hermit souls that live withdrawn / In the place of their self-content" are the first two lines of a poem by Sam Walter Foss. What is its title?

85. In "The Owl and the Fox" (author unknown), where does the fox live?

Answers

1. ". . . a buckskin shirt that was glazed with dirt . . ."
2. "You elegant fowl!"
3. Blake (or Blakey).
4. "If you can keep your head when all about you," In Rudyard Kipling's "If—."
5. Lou.
6. "America, the Beautiful."
7. "The Land of Counterpane."
8. North Church.
9. The little toy soldier and the little toy dog.

10. "'Tis the Last Rose of Summer."
11. "The Vampire," by Rudyard Kipling.
12. "Be the labor great or small/Do it well or not at all."
13. "Up above the world so high/Like a diamond in the sky."
14. "Just then flew down a monstrous crow, as black as a tar barrel/ Which frightened both the heroes so, they quite forgot their quarrel."
15. "'Twas my forefather's hand/That placed it near his cot."
16. Ella Wheeler Wilcox.
17. "Thus the little minutes/Humble though they be/Make the mighty ages/Of eternity."
18. "It's the steady, quiet, plodding ones/Who win in the lifelong race."
19. A wedding between the fair Ellen and a bridegroom who was "a laggard in love, and a dastard in war."
20. "Wynken and Blynken are two little eyes/And Nod is a little head."
21. "A stranger," later identified in the poem as Ibrahim, who had killed Yussouf's son.
22. He is the prisoner in "Curfew Must Not Ring Tonight." He is to be executed at the ringing of the curfew bell but is saved by Bessie, the girl who loves him, and Cromwell.
23. "Rags," also the title of this poem by Edmund Vance Cooke.
24. 90 years.
25. "The less he spoke the more he heard/Why can't we all be like that bird?"
26. Laces, ivory, gold, silks, old trees, and old streets.
27. "Jest 'fore Christmas."
28. "She walks in beauty, like the night/Of cloudless climes and starry skies." The poem is "She Walks in Beauty," by Lord Byron.
29. "... 'Twas the emblem of labor, my dad's dinner pail." The poem is "My Dad's Dinner Pail."
30. Shelter; bread; wine.
31. "If you can fill the unforgiving minute/With sixty seconds' worth of distance run/Yours is the Earth and everything that's in it/ And—which is more—you'll be a Man, my son!"
32. Dogs. (The lines are from Hally Carrington Brent's "I Think I Know No Finer Things than Dogs.")
33. Robert W. Service ("The Spell of the Yukon").
34. "Lochinvar."
35. "Somerset."
36. "Like an old coat, all tattered and torn."
37. "... because it was/The middle of the night."
38. "Boots—boots—boots—boots—movin' up and down again!"
39. Ermine.
40. From the pawnshop.
41. 4–2. When Casey struck out to end the game, Mudville had two men on base.
42. "Crack a nut."
43. "The sacred river."

44. "O beautiful for spacious skies/For amber waves of grain."
45. "Jabberwocky."
46. Summer ("'Twas a balmy summer evening").
47. Daffodils, in his poem of that name.
48. "Sea Fever."
49. Robert Louis Stevenson.
50. Mabel.
51. "... when the leaves hang trembling ... when the trees bow down their heads."
52. "The Raggedy Man."
53. "To a rag and a bone and a hank of hair/(We called her the woman who did not care)/But the fool he called her his lady fair."
54. "To be, or not to be: that is the question" (from Shakespeare's "Hamlet").
55. "And lose, and start again at your beginnings/And never breathe a word about your loss."
56. "The truth about the cat and pup/Is this: They ate each other up!"
57. "A wooden shoe."
58. "... the people who lift and the people who lean," In the poem "Lifting and Leaning."
59. "That it ill behoves any of us/To find fault with the rest of us." The author of this poem is unknown.
60. Madeline.
61. "The moon was a ghostly galleon tossed upon cloudy seas."
62. "But Heaven will protect the Working Girl," from the poem of that name.
63. Mudville.
64. Edith; golden.
65. The children are "a-list'nin to the witch-tales 'at Annie tells about."
66. Lowell and Cabot.
67. "Or walk with kings—nor lose the common touch."
68. He is "fair and wise and good and gay."
69. "Prison cells of pride."
70. "Curfew Must Not Ring Tonight."
71. "An angel writing in a book of gold."
72. "But I can tell you, anyhow/I'd rather see than be one."
73. The Walrus, in Lewis Carroll's "The Walrus and the Carpenter."
74. "The Shooting of Dan McGrew."
75. "A stumbling block—or a steppingstone."
76. They "sat up in the light-house tower."
77. September.
78. The Squirrel, in "The Mountain and the Squirrel."
79. Islington.
80. "... in an oak."
81. Emily Dickinson ("Indian Summer").
82. "Wednesday's child is full of woe/Thursday's child has far to go."
83. "A Dutch Lullaby."
84. "The House by the Side of the Road."
85. "Under the rocks at the foot of a huge old tree."

GOVERNMENT

1. During the 1930s, many government agencies were created and called by their initials. One of these was the CCC, which provided work for more than 2 million men in its nine years of existence. What did CCC stand for?

2. What were the symbol and the slogan of the National Recovery Administration?

3. The WPA was a federal agency founded in 1935 to provide work and instruction for millions of Americans. For what did those initials stand?

4. The letters OWI stood for what wartime government agency?

5. The first federal minimum wage law went into effect in October 1938. How much was the minimum?

6. J. Edgar Hoover became head of the Bureau of Investigation, now called Federal Bureau of Investigation, in May 1924. Who preceded him in the job?

7. What is the nickname of the 20th Amendment to the Constitution (effective 1933)?

8. Name the famous American immigration depot that was open from 1890 to 1954.

9. In the Preamble to the Constitution, what are the eight words immediately following "We the People of the United States"?

10. Income-tax withholding started in 1943. What was the percentage withheld from wages and salaries?

11. Containment by the U.S. of Soviet expansion after World War II was known as what kind of "doctrine"?

12. The CCC was established in 1933 to provide jobs for otherwise jobless men between the ages of 18 and what?

13. Who was the Supreme Court Justice who resigned in 1916 and was reappointed, as Chief Justice, in 1930?

14. U.S. Treasury Secretary Salmon P. Chase introduced what noted motto, in 1865?

15. Who was named chairman of the House Committee In-

vestigating Un-American Activities when it was established in 1938?

16. Only one member of Congress voted against declaration of war by the U.S. against Japan after the Japanese attack on Pearl Harbor in 1941. The member?

17. During the U.S. Civil War, the number of Justices on the Supreme Court was increased to nine. How many had sat on the court before the change?

18. What amendment to the Constitution put the "noble experiment" into effect?

19. Charles G. Dawes was elected to what office in 1924?

20. How many arrows are held in the left talon of the American eagle on the face of the Great Seal of the U.S.?

21. The term "gerrymander" came into use in the early part of the 19th century when what governor of Massachusetts realigned voting districts?

22. The constitutional convention opened in Philadelphia in May 1787. Who presided?

23. Whose civil rights were restored by the Amnesty Act of 1872?

24. What post was filled by Andrew Mellon after he was Secretary of the Treasury?

25. Samuel Osgood was the first person to serve in what cabinet post?

26. What noted federal act was passed into law on August 14, 1935?

Answers

1. Civilian Conservation Corps.
2. The Blue Eagle; "We do our part."
3. Works Progress Administration.
4. Office of War Information.
5. 25 cents an hour.
6. William J. Burns.
7. "Lame Duck." The amendment brought back inauguration dates for the President, Vice-President, and members of Congress from March to January.
8. Ellis Island.
9. ". . . in order to form a more perfect union . . ."
10. 20 percent.
11. Truman Doctrine.
12. 25.
13. Charles Evans Hughes.

14. "In God We Trust."
15. Representative Martin Dies (Dem.), Tex.
16. Miss Jeannette Rankin of Montana, who had also voted against declaring war on Germany in 1917.
17. Six.
18. The 18th, or Prohibition, Amendment.
19. Vice-President of the U.S., with President Coolidge.
20. 13.
21. Elbridge Gerry.
22. George Washington.
23. Citizens of Southern states. Several hundred former Confederate leaders were excluded.
24. Ambassador to Great Britain.
25. Postmaster General.
26. Social Security Act.

CHILDREN'S STORIES AND NURSERY RHYMES

1. Identify the story from which this passage is taken:
" 'Ahai!' said the old woman, 'and I'll be bound to say,
my dear, you'd like to go too. Ay, so I thought. Come,
then, there's no time to waste. Night's speeding on. Put
on your own and we'll be off to the Palace at once.' "

2. According to the children's song, during what period of
the day do we go round the mulberry bush?

3. "Sing a song of sixpence / A pocket full of rye / Four
and twenty blackbirds / Baked in a pie" is the first
stanza of a nursery rhyme. What is the next stanza?

4. In the nursery rhyme entitled "Teeny-Tiny," what does
the teeny-tiny woman answer to the teeny-tiny voice
that calls out, "Give me my bone"?

5. Complete this nursery rhyme: "Elsie Marley is grown
so fine / She won't get up to feed the swine . . ."

6. How did Jack get the magic beans that grew into a high
beanstalk?

7. According to the rhyme, Simple Simon was sure he
could catch a dickeybird. Why was he certain?

8. What does Little Red Riding-Hood take to her grand-
mother?

9. In the story of the Three Little Pigs, one of the pigs is
carrying a butter churn when he sees the wolf coming.
How does the pig get by?

10. In the story of "Snow White and the Seven Dwarfs,"
what is the relationship between Snow White and the
Queen who periodically asked a mirror who was the
fairest in the land?

11. According to the rhyme, what are little boys made of?

12. What question is asked in "Peter Piper"?

13. In the rhyme "Pussy in the Well," who put Pussy in the
well and who pulled her out?

14. "Tell your momma to hold her tongue" is the first line
of a childhood chant. What is the remaining line?

15. Complete the childhood chant "It's raining, it's pouring."

16. In Hans Christian Andersen's story "The Nightingale," what replaced the nightingale who sang to the emperor?

17. "There was an old woman who lived in a shoe / She had so many children she didn't know what to do" is from the rhyme "The Old Woman in a Shoe." The next line tells what the children were given to eat. What was it?

18. In the rhyme which begins "One, two—buckle my shoe," what follows "Seven, eight"?

19. Add the remaining two lines to the following nursery rhyme, entitled "Pussy Cat:" "Pussy cat, pussy cat / Where have you been / I've been to London / To look at the Queen / Pussy cat, pussy cat / What did you there . . ."

20. In "Little Bo-Peep," what do the sheep leave behind them?

21. What is the final line of every verse of "London Bridge"?

22. In the story of "Jack and the Beanstalk," where did Jack hide the first two times he climbed the beanstalk and went to the ogre's house?

23. Add the final line to this nursery rhyme: "It's raining, it's pouring / The old man's snoring / He got into bed / And bumped his head . . ."

24. Why did Beauty go to the castle of the Beast in the fairy tale "Beauty and the Beast"?

25. Complete this nursery rhyme: "A diller, a dollar / A ten o'clock scholar / What makes you come so soon . . ."

26. How many dogs are there in the story "The Tinder Box," by Hans Christian Andersen?

27. In a nursery rhyme, for what did Charley Barley sell his wife?

28. "A Sunshiney Shower" is the title and first line of a two-line nursery rhyme. What is the second line?

29. In the story "The Little House," by Virginia Lee Burton, what good thing happened to the house at the end?

30. By what name is the cat known in the children's story of "Dick Whittington and His Cat"?

31. Complete the children's rhyme which beings: "Doctor Foster went to Gloucester / In a shower of rain . . ."

32. From where did Snow White get food when she came upon a tiny hut in a wooden glen?

33. After escaping from a wicked fairy, Hansel and Gretel

lived in a great wood where Hansel drank from a brook and was turned into what animal? (This second part of the story of Hansel and Gretel is known as "The Brother and Sister.")

34. What was the name of the cow Jack traded for some beans in "Jack and the Beanstalk"?

35. In the Brer Rabbit stories, what "contrapshun" does Brer Fox set up to catch Brer Rabbit?

36. Complete this stanza of the Simple Simon rhyme: "Simple Simon went to look / If plums grew on a thistle . . ."

37. What other rabbits are mentioned by name in the children's story "The Tale of Peter Rabbit"?

38. According to a nursery rhyme, "The Queen of Hearts / She made some tarts / All on a summer's day." Who stole them?

39. With whom did Cinderella live?

40. In what kind of house does the witch in "Hansel and Gretel" live?

41. What foods are mentioned in the nursery rhyme "Little Tommy Tucker"?

42. "Jack Spratt could eat no fat / His wife could eat no lean" are the opening lines of the nursery rhyme "Jack Spratt and His Wife." What are the remaining two lines?

43. Where does "Peter, Peter, pumpkin eater" put his wife?

44. In the "Jack and Jill" rhyme, Jack falls down a hill and breaks his crown. He gets up and runs home. What happens then?

Answers

1. "Cinderella and the Glass Slipper."
2. "So early in the morning."
3. "When the pie was opened/The birds began to sing/Was not that a dainty dish/To set before the king?"
4. "TAKE IT!"
5. "But lies in bed till eight or nine/Lazy Elsie Marley."
6. He traded the family cow to a funny-looking old man for five magic beans.
7. "Because he's got a little salt/To put upon its tail."
8. A cake and a small jar of butter.
9. He gets into the churn and rolls past the wolf.
10. The Queen is Snow White's stepmother. She dislikes Snow White because the magic mirror says that Snow White is fairer than the Queen.
11. "Frogs and snails/And puppy-dogs' tails." (Little girls are made of

"Sugar and spice/And all things nice.")

12. "Where's the peck of pickled pepper/Peter Piper picked?"

13. Little Tommy Lynn put her in and Little Johnny Stout pulled her out. (Versions differ, however. Others mention Tommy Thin and Tommy Stout, and Tommy Green and Tommy Trout.)

14. "She had a feller when she was young."

15. "The old man is snoring."

16. An artificial nightingale. (The real bird later returned and sang to the emperor.)

17. "She gave them some broth without any bread."

18. "Lay them straight."

19. "I frightened a little mouse/Under her chair."

20. Their tails.

21. "My fair lady."

22. In the oven, thanks to the ogre's wife.

23. "And couldn't get up in the morning."

24. Her father had stayed in the castle during a tiring journey, and before he left he picked a rose to take to Beauty. The Beast, really a prince under enchantment, asked the father to promise the Beast one of his daughters so that he might be forgiven for taking the rose.

25. "You used to come at ten o'clock/But now you come at noon."

26. Three—one with eyes as big as saucers; a second with eyes as big as millstones; and a third with eyes each as big as the Round Tower.

27. Three duck eggs.

28. "Won't last half an hour."

29. The Little House, which had been in the country, saw the city grow up around it, but in the end it was moved back to the countryside where it again was very happy.

30. Miss Puss.

31. "He stepped in a puddle/Right up to his middle/And never went there again."

32. The little house, home of the seven dwarfs, contained a table set with food and drink for seven. Snow White took a little food from each plate and drank a little wine from each goblet.

33. A fawn.

34. Milky-White.

35. A Tar-Baby.

36. "He pricked his fingers very much/Which made poor Simon whistle."

37. Flopsy, Mopsy, and Cottontail.

38. The Knave of Hearts.

39. With two half-sisters according to one version of the fairy tale; but with two half-sisters and a stepmother in another.

40. One made of gingerbread.

41. White bread and butter.

42. "And so betwixt them both you see/They licked the platter clean."

43. "In a pumpkin shell."

44. "They put him to bed and plastered his head/With vinegar and brown paper."

PLAYS

1. What is the title of the play about members of the Vanderhof-Sycamore family by George S. Kaufman and Moss Hart?

2. Jeeter Lester was a character in what novel, play, and movie?

3. Name the play in progress at Ford's Theatre when President Lincoln was shot.

4. Name the actor who won fame during the late 19th century by portraying Rip Van Winkle for 40 years.

5. Who is the Anne of Maxwell Anderson's play "Anne of the Thousand Days"?

6. "The Tragical History of Dr. Faustus" was written about four centuries ago by Christopher Marlowe. In this play, Faustus pledges his soul to the Devil. What is he promised in return?

7. Who starred as Killer Mears in the 1930 hit "The Last Mile"?

8. "The Aldrich Family" of radio fame was based on what hit Broadway play?

9. What is the name of the character in the play "All the King's Men," by Robert Penn Warren, who is based on former Governor Huey Long of Louisiana?

10. The setting of "The Teahouse of the August Moon" is the island of Okinawa. This play, by John Patrick, is narrated by a native. What is his name?

11. The play "I Remember Mama" depicts the life of a Norwegian-American family in what city?

12. Louis O. Coxe and Robert Chapman wrote a play in which the entire setting is the "HMS Indomitable." What is the play's title?

13. A play entitled "The Drunkard" ran for decades. What was unusual about the way the audiences were treated?

14. Do you know the title of the play by Mary Chase in which a middle-aged bachelor meets and becomes the inseparable friend of a six-foot-tall rabbit?

15. How do the girls who dance in the woods in Arthur

Miller's "The Crucible" avoid punishment normally decreed by the Puritan moral code?

16. Name the Broadway play and movie in which Humphrey Bogart portrayed Duke Mantee.

17. Who portrayed Mrs. Martin in the stage and film productions of "Dead End"?

18. Name the popular Civil War era play about a married woman turned out by her husband "never to darken the door again."

19. Erskine Caldwell wrote the novel "Tobacco Road." Who wrote the play adaptation of the same name?

20. The original cast of what late 1940s play included Henry Fonda, William Harrigan, Robert Keith, and David Wayne?

Answers

1. "You Can't Take It with You."
2. "Tobacco Road."
3. "Our American Cousin."
4. Joseph Jefferson, known as the "dean of the American stage."
5. Anne Boleyn, second wife of Henry VIII of England.
6. Twenty-four years of earthly power and delight.
7. Spencer Tracy.
8. "What a Life!"
9. Willie Stark.
10. Sakini.
11. San Francisco.
12. "Billy Budd."
13. They were treated to beer and pretzels during performances.
14. "Harvey."
15. They declare themselves victims of the devil and wrongfully accuse several women of witchcraft.
16. "The Petrified Forest."
17. Marjorie Main.
18. "East Lynne."
19. John Kirkland.
20. "Mister Roberts."

MUSIC

1. What was Ruth Etting's "moon" theme song?
2. What singer has been associated with the signature song "Wheel of Fortune"?
3. Name the best-known singer with the Ted Weems band.
4. Who was the bandleader of the "Musical Knights"?
5. Eileen Barton made one million-selling recording, in 1950. What is it?
6. Within three years, what was the year all of these songs came out: "Nature Boy," "A Little Bird Told Me," "Buttons and Bows," and "Tennessee Waltz"?
7. Name the only million-selling recording made by Clyde McCoy and his orchestra.
8. During his earlier years, what did Rudy Vallee hold in his hands as he sang?
9. The author of "Hey, Good Lookin'," a country and western singer, made a hit recording of it in 1951. Name him.
10. Name the western entertainer associated with the theme song "Back in the Saddle Again."
11. "Donkey Serenade" was introduced in the 1937 movie "The Firefly." Who sang it?
12. In a poll conducted by the "New York World-Telegram," Bing Crosby was voted the top male popular singer of 1938. Who came in second: Frank Parker, Nelson Eddy, Kenny Baker, or Lanny Ross?
13. "Rock Around the Clock" was the second million-selling recording by Bill Haley and His Comets. What was the preceding million seller?
14. Name the orchestra that made a hit recording in 1941 of "Pennsylvania 6–5000."
15. Name the polka that was the biggest seller in sheet music in 1939 and probably the most popular song during World War II.
16. A singer whose real name is June Webb made a big hit recording of "Cry Me a River" in 1955, for Liberty. By what name is she known?
17. One of the big hits of 1917 was "Oh, Johnny, Oh,

Johnny, Oh!" It made a comeback in 1939 when a recording sold about two million copies. Who sang "Oh, Johnny" in that 1939 recording?

18. "If You Knew Susie" was an Eddie Cantor favorite but it was introduced by someone else. Who?

19. Who played the trombone in Kid Ory's Original Creole Jazz Band and in Jelly Roll Morton's Red Hot Peppers?

20. What is the name of the sister in the title of the shimmy song by Armand Piron and Peter Bocage?

21. Can you name Edith Piaf's signature song?

22. Who wrote "Riverboat Shuffle" and "Washboard Blues"?

23. Name the song by Irving Berlin, about a pretty girl, which was in the "Ziegfeld Follies of 1919."

24. Sonny Greer, Joe Jones, and Cliff Leeman are known for playing what musical instrument?

25. Johnny Dodds, Pee Wee Russell, and Artie Shaw are among the top jazz musicians of all time. What was their regular instrument?

26. "There's Yes, Yes in Your Eyes," by Cliff Friend and Joseph H. Santly, a 1924 number, was legally adjudged a plagiarism of what older song?

27. What famous singer gave her first concert in the U.S. in September 1850, at the Castle Garden in New York City?

28. What song, long associated with him, did Al Jolson introduce in the 1921 musical "Bombo"?

29. A song entitled "The Story of a Rose" is a favorite of quartets today under a different name. What is it?

30. Within five years, what was the year when all these songs came out: "Peg o' My Heart," "All Aboard for Dixie Land," and "Be My Little Baby Bumble Bee"?

31. What song, written in 1927 by Walter Donaldson and George Whiting, was popularized by Gene Austin via Victor Records?

32. "Hezzie" (Paul Trietsch) was one of the Hoosier Hot Shots and he played three musical instruments. Name at least one.

33. The 1928 song "Together," by De Sylva, Brown, and Henderson, made a comeback in a 1944 movie starring Claudette Colbert, Joseph Cotten, Jennifer Jones, and Shirley Temple. The picture?

34. Do you know what musical instrument Glenn Miller played?

35. Probably the hit song of 1944 was composed by Irving K. Hill, was popularized by Hildegarde and Frank Sinatra, and was on radio's "Hit Parade" for half the year. What is the song?

36. Who wrote "St. Louis Blues," a song published in 1914?

37. "Be My Love" was a hit song especially associated with what singer?

38. What instrument did Oscar Moore play with the original King Cole Trio?

39. How many relatives are mentioned in "Pretty Baby," by Egbert Van Alstyne and Gus Kahn?

40. What type of music gained popularity in the mid-1930s and afterward? It was featured by the bands of Hal Kemp, the Dorsey Brothers, Dick Haymes, and Eddy Duchin, among others.

41. What is the title of the song, popularized by Jo Stafford, that has the line "Good-bye Joe me gotta go me oh my oh"?

42. Name one of the first two songs Elvis Presley recorded, on the Sun label in 1954.

43. What is the name of the song, popularized in 1945, that includes a kind of alcoholic beverage and the name of a soft drink in the title?

44. In the song "Swinging on a Star," from the film "Going My Way," what line follows "Would you like to swing on a star?"

45. The song "Darling, Je Vous Aime Beaucoup" was adopted in the mid-1930s as what entertainer's theme?

46. What is the title of the song about roses which has the tune of "The Old-Time Religion"? It was popular during the 1940s.

47. What operatic musical featured "I Got Plenty o' Nuttin' " and "It Ain't Necessarily So"?

48. Complete this title: "Where Did Robinson Crusoe Go with . . ."

49. Martha, Helvetia, and Connee (originally Connie) won renown as what vocal and instrumental trio of sisters?

50. Name the entertainer who made "My Bill" famous.

51. More than a million copies of the sheet music of "Baby Face" were sold in the mid-1920s, but it was during the

late 1940s that a hit recording of the song came out. Whose orchestra made the recording?

52. In what decade of this century did "Who's Sorry Now?" and "Sugar Blues" come out?

53. Freda Gibbson, a singer, was known by what other name?

54. Complete the title of this song written more than a half century ago: "My Home Town Is a One-Horse Town But . . ."

55. Identify Irving Aaronson's Commanders.

56. Name the only recording by the Harmonicats that reached the million level in sales.

57. Complete this song title: "Way Down in Iowa . . ."

58. The song "There's a Rainbow 'Round My Shoulder" was written in the late 1920s by three men. Name at least one of them.

59. Name the room and the New York City hotel where Vincent Lopez and his orchestra played for years.

60. Before he started his own band, Skinnay Ennis was a popular singer with whose band?

61. Whose band had the theme song "Snowfall"?

62. The writer of "Big Bad John" made a hit recording of it. Who is he?

63. What bandleader married Georgia Carroll, who sang in his band at the time?

64. Larry Funk led a "Band of a Thousand ———."

65. Complete this song title, written in 1915: "There's a Broken Heart for Every ——— ——— ———."

66. Who wrote the music of "Star Dust"?

67. Ella Fitzgerald got her big-time singing start with what band, in the mid-1930s?

68. Name the orchestra leader known as the "Idol of the Air Waves."

69. Complete the title of at least two of these three songs from the year 1936: "I've Got You ——— ——— ———," "One, Two, ——— ——— ———," and "Stompin' at the ———."

70. What orchestra is associated with the theme song "Nola"?

71. What 1952 song by Bennie Benjamin and George Weiss did Kay Starr immensely popularize?

72. What was the signature song of Paul Whiteman?

73. In 1946, Spike Jones and His City Slickers made a com-

ical recording of "Glow Worm," but in 1952 another group made a hit recording of the same song. The group?

74. Complete the title of this 1928 song: "I Faw Down ———— ———— ————!"

75. In 1947, Art Mooney and his orchestra made a recording of a 20-year-old song. The record, featuring Mike Pingatore on the banjo, became a big hit. The title?

76. The middle strain of a 1922 hit song echoes the Westminster Chime of London's Big Ben. The song?

77. Name Cab Calloway's signature song.

78. During what decade of the 20th century did these songs come out: "Row, Row, Row," "Where the Twilight Comes to Kiss the Rose 'Good Night,'" and "It's a Long, Long Way to Tipperary"?

79. Bandleader Ray McKinley sang and played what instrument?

80. Name the band with the theme song "Tuxedo Junction."

81. Who wrote and made a hit record in 1940 of "San Antonio Rose"?

82. Fill in the name of the bandleader: "———— ———— and His Gramercy Five."

83. Do you know Art Mooney's theme?

84. Complete this song title: "Oh, How She Could Yacki Hacki ———— ————."

85. What was Henry Busse's theme song? His instrument?

86. What was the theme song of Les Paul and Mary Ford?

87. Whose orchestra made a hit recording of "Boogie Woogie" in 1938?

88. In 1940, trumpeter Harry James left whose orchestra to form his own group?

89. Who made a hit recording in 1947 of the song "Confess," backed with "Love Somebody"?

90. In what decade of this century did these songs come out: "Tiger Rag," "Macnamara's Band," and "Where the Black-eyed Susans Grow"?

91. What is Fred Waring's theme song?

92. The sister of Guy, Victor, Carmen, and Leibert Lombardo sang in Guy's orchestra. Her name?

93. What bandleader and his singing wife were billed as "Mr. and Mrs. Swing"?

94. What was Jimmy Dorsey's theme song?

95. With whose band did Harry Babbitt and Ginny Sims sing in the 1940s?

96. Do you know Harry James's signature song?

97. Who was called "Ukulele Ike"?

98. "Song of the Islands," by Charles King, was popular in 1915. To what islands does it refer?

99. "And over one kidney / Was a bird's-eye view of Sydney" are lines from what song?

100. Name the instrument played by jazz bandleader Phil Napoleon.

101. The song " 'Swonderful," by George and Ira Gershwin, was introduced in what musical?

102. Within two years, name the year when all the following four novelty songs were published: "A-Tisket A-Tasket," "Stop Beating 'Round the Mulberry Bush," "Jeepers Creepers," and "Flat-Foot Floogey with the Floy Floy."

103. "Ragging the Scale" is music written by Edward Claypoole especially for what instrument?

104. Who wrote the lyrics of "The Atchison, Topeka, and the Santa Fe," "Ac-cent-tchuate the Positive," and "Dreams"?

105. A popular song 30 years ago was "Besame Mucho." What does the title mean?

106. Fill in the missing word in these song titles: "Wang, Wang ————," "Bye, Bye, ————," and "I Gotta Right to Sing the ————."

107. Name at least two of the four different musical instruments played by brothers Jack, Charlie, and Cub Teagarden, and sister Norma.

108. A popular song title years ago requested someone named Richard to do something. What?

109. Who wrote the melody of "Tea for Two"?

110. A bandleader of yesteryear referred to himself as the "Old Maestro." His name?

111. The song "Some of These Days" brings what singer to mind?

112. Entertainer Bob Burns brought recognition to an unusual musical instrument. What was it called?

113. Who wrote the hit "Don't Fence Me In"?

114. It is not definitely known whether Emperor Nero played a musical instrument during the burning of

Rome in A.D. 64. If the legend is true, what instrument did Nero probably play?

115. Name the singing group that brought popularity in later years to the 1933 song "Bei Mir Bist Du Schoen."

116. The songs "Kitty from Kansas City," "Stein Song," and "I'm Just a Vagabond Lover" bring what singer to mind?

117. Name the musical instrument played by David Rubinoff and the word used to describe it.

118. What well-known song by Harry Ruby and Bert Kalmar was introduced in the 1930 movie "Check and Double Check," starring Amos 'n' Andy?

119. By what name was the musical combination of Kenneth and Paul Prietsch and Otto Ward known?

120. What composer-pianist-singer comes to mind when one thinks of the songs "Ain't Misbehavin' " and "Honeysuckle Rose"?

121. In 1924, a 30-year-old songwriter and musician wrote these hits: "Spain," "The One I Love Belongs to Somebody Else," "I'll See You in My Dreams," and "It Had to Be You." Name him.

122. Hoagy Carmichael wrote the melody of the all-time favorite song "Star Dust." Who wrote the words?

123. Whose names are mentioned in the 1905 song hit "In My Merry Oldsmobile," with words and music by Gus Edwards and Vincent Bryan?

124. Stephen Foster wrote the song that begins "Way down upon the Swanee River." What is the title?

125. The words and music of the song "I Can't Give You Anything But Love" are by Dorothy Fields and Jimmy McHugh. In what musical was this song presented for the first time?

126. A 1931 song, "As Time Goes By," was revived in 1943 in the movie "Casablanca," starring Ingrid Bergman and Humphrey Bogart, and became a hit. Who sang it in the picture and what other song did he sing in "Casablanca"?

127. What four words go before "Jingle, Jangle, Jingle" in the song of that title?

128. Name the song that was written in 1934 for the movie "Argentina Night" but wasn't introduced until ten years later in the film "Hollywood Canteen."

129. Patti Page recorded a song in 1950 that became a big

hit, with sales of several million copies. What is the title and on what label was it recorded?

130. In 1917, Irving Berlin wrote a song called "Smile and Show Your Dimple." The song was a flop but the melody from it was used again by Mr. Berlin in 1933 for a song which has become one of the all-time favorites. Its title?

131. One of the most inspiring songs from World War II was "Coming in on a Wing and a Prayer." Who wrote it?

132. The song "Heartaches" came out in 1931 but won its greatest popularity in 1947 through a recording by whose band?

133. The song "Mammy" was a trademark of Al Jolson, but who first sang it publicly?

134. Do you know the title of the campaign song of former Louisiana Governor Jimmie Davis?

135. What is Bing Crosby's best-selling recording?

136. Name the musical instrument played expertly by Mitch Miller.

137. Phil Harris popularized a song in 1950 in which three loud drumbeats drowned him out every time he mentioned what he saw on a beach. What is the song's title?

138. Who wrote the words of these songs: "Me and My Shadow," "There's a Rainbow 'Round My Shoulder," and "I Wanna Be Loved"?

139. According to a famous song, in what State do "the cotton and the corn and the taters grow"?

140. Who was known as "The Warbling Banjoist" early in his radio career?

141. Name at least one of the team of two songwriters responsible for the following songs: "Let a Smile Be Your Umbrella," "Wedding Bells Are Breaking Up That Old Gang of Mine," and "When I Take My Sugar to Tea."

142. Name the leader of the band described as having "breezy rhythm."

143. Name two of the three singing Pickens Sisters.

144. What song, with a measurement of time in its title, was made popular by Gracie Fields in the late 1940s?

145. Name at least three of the six original members of the Country Music Hall of Fame.

Answers

1. "Shine On, Harvest Moon."
2. Kay Starr.
3. Perry Como.
4. Horace Heidt.
5. "If I Knew You Were Coming I'd Have Baked a Cake."
6. 1948.
7. "Sugar Blues" (adopted as his signature song).
8. A megaphone.
9. Hank Williams.
10. Gene Autry.
11. Allan Jones.
12. Kenny Baker. (A "Radio Guide" poll for that year had Baker fourth, behind Crosby, Jerry Cooper, and Donald Novis.)
13. "Shake, Rattle, and Roll."
14. Glenn Miller's. The title was the phone number of the Pennsylvania Hotel in New York, where the Miller band played.
15. "Beer Barrel Polka."
16. Julie London.
17. Bonnie Baker.
18. Al Jolson (1925).
19. Kid Ory.
20. "Kate." The line is "I wish I could shimmy like my sister Kate."
21. "La Vie en Rose."
22. Hoagy Carmichael.
23. "A Pretty Girl Is Like a Melody."
24. Drums.
25. Clarinet.
26. "Without You the World Don't Seem the Same."
27. Jenny Lind.
28. "April Showers."
29. "Heart of My Heart, I Love You."
30. 1913.
31. "My Blue Heaven."
32. Zither, whistle, and washboard.
33. "Since You Went Away."
34. Trombone.
35. "I'll Be Seeing You."
36. W. C. Handy.
37. Mario Lanza.
38. Guitar.
39. Four: "And I'd like to be your sister, brother, dad, and mother too."
40. Swing.
41. "Jumbalaya."
42. "That's All Right, Mama"; "Blue Moon Kentucky."
43. "Rum and Coca-Cola."
44. "Carry moonbeams home in a jar."
45. Hildegarde.
46. "One Dozen Roses."
47. "Porgy and Bess."

48. "Friday on Saturday Night?"
49. Boswell Sisters.
50. Helen Morgan.
51. Art Mooney's.
52. 1920s (specifically, 1923).
53. Georgia Gibbs.
54. "It's Big Enough for Me."
55. A band of several decades ago that played primarily in theaters.
56. "Peg o' My Heart," a song written in 1913 and recorded by the trio in 1947.
57. "I'm Going to Hide Away."
58. Al Jolson, Billy Rose, and Dave Dreyer.
59. Grill Room of the Hotel Taft.
60. Hal Kemp's.
61. Claude Thornhill's.
62. Jimmy Dean.
63. Kay Kyser.
64. "Melodies."
65. "Light on Broadway."
66. Hoagy Carmichael.
67. Chick Webb's.
68. Jan Garber.
69. "Under My Skin"; "Button Your Shoe"; "Savoy."
70. Vincent Lopez's.
71. "Wheel of Fortune."
72. "Rhapsody in Blue."
73. The Mills Brothers, with Hal McIntyre and orchestra.
74. "An' Go Boom!"
75. "I'm Looking Over a Four-Leaf Clover."
76. "Three O'Clock in the Morning" (Julian Robledo and Dorothy Terriss).
77. "Minnie the Moocher."
78. The "tens" (1912).
79. Drums.
80. Chick Webb's.
81. Bob Wills.
82. Artie Shaw.
83. "Sunset to Sunrise."
84. "Wicki Woo."
85. "Hot Lips"; trumpet.
86. "How High the Moon."
87. Tommy Dorsey's.
88. Benny Goodman's.
89. Doris Day (with Buddy Clark).
90. The "tens" (1917).
91. "Sleep."
92. Rose Marie.
93. Red and Mildred Norvo.
94. "Contrasts."
95. Kay Kyser's.
96. "Ciribiribin."
97. Cliff Edwards.

98. Hawaiian.
99. "The Tattooed Lady."
100. Trumpet.
101. "Funny Face" (1927).
102. 1938.
103. Piano.
104. Johnny Mercer.
105. "Kiss Me Much." (The title is in Spanish.)
106. Blues.
107. Trombone, trumpet, drums, and piano respectively.
108. "Open the Door, Richard."
109. Vincent Youmans.
110. Ben Bernie.
111. Sophie Tucker.
112. Bazooka.
113. Cole Porter.
114. Lyre. Some people think "Nero fiddled while Rome burned," but the violin was not in use at the time.
115. Andrews Sisters (Patty, LaVerne, and Maxine).
116. Rudy Vallee.
117. Magic violin.
118. "Three Little Words."
119. Hoosier Hot Shots.
120. Thomas (Fats) Waller.
121. Isham Jones.
122. Mitchell Parish.
123. Johnny Steele and his girl friend, Lucile.
124. "The Old Folks at Home."
125. "Blackbirds of 1928."
126. Dooley Wilson; "It Had to Be You."
127. "I've got spurs that . . ."
128. "Don't Fence Me In," by Cole Porter. (The Andrews Sisters sing it in "Hollywood Canteen.")
129. "Tennessee Waltz"; Mercury.
130. "Easter Parade."
131. Jimmy McHugh and Harold Adamson.
132. That of Ted Weens.
133. Comedian Bill Frawley, in vaudeville.
134. "You Are My Sunshine," which he helped write.
135. "White Christmas."
136. Oboe.
137. "The Thing."
138. Billy Rose.
139. Virginia. The song is "Carry Me Back to Old Virginny."
140. Arthur Godfrey.
141. Sammy Fain and Irving Kahal.
142. Lou Breese.
143. Jane, Helen, and Patty.
144. "Now Is the Hour."
145. Fred Rose; Jimmie Rodgers; Hank Williams; Roy Acuff; Tex Ritter; Ernest Tubb.

QUOTATIONS

1. One of the best-known remarks by Mae West is her "Come up 'n' see me sometime." In what theatrical presentation did she say it?
2. Who made the statement: "I tell you ... all politics is applesauce"?
3. Quote the line that precedes the familiar "And fired the shot heard round the world."
4. Give the meaning of the Latin phrase that accompanies the Metro-Goldwyn-Mayer trademark of Leo the Lion.
5. Name the book by Sinclair Lewis from which the following is taken: "A sensational event was changing from the brown suit to the gray the contents of his pockets. He was earnest about these objects. They were of eternal importance, like baseball or the Republican Party."
6. Anita Loos wrote that "Gentlemen always seem to remember blondes." In what book did she write this?
7. Name the newspaperman who said, "If you go long enough without a bath even the fleas will let you alone."
8. Who said, in "The Disappearance of Literature," that "a classic is something that everybody wants to have read and nobody wants to read"?
9. Who wrote: "The ripest peach is highest on the tree"?
10. U.S. Secretary of War Edwin Stanton is credited with the remark "Now he belongs to the ages." What was the occasion of his statement?
11. A syndicated newspaper columnist once wrote that "a comedian can only last till he either takes himself serious or his audience takes him serious." Who made this observation?
12. William Shakespeare wrote: "Some are born great, some achieve greatness, and some have greatness thrust upon them." This quotation is from which of his plays?
13. Mark Twain wrote: "If you pick up a starving dog and make him prosperous, he will not bite you. This is the principal difference between a dog and a man." In which of his writings is this?

14. "Now would I give a thousand furlongs of sea for an acre of barren ground" is by William Shakespeare. In which of his writings does this appear?

15. Who said, "Everything is funny as long as it is happening to somebody else"?

16. Who said, "There will never be a system invented which will do away with the necessity for work"?

17. Name the actress who said, "I want to be alone."

18. Who said, "There's a sucker born every minute"?

19. What politician said, "Every man is a king"?

20. Who wrote: "A straw vote only shows which way the hot air blows"?

21. Who wrote: "It brings up happy old days when I was only a farmer and not an agriculturist"?

22. Name the actress associated with the line, "That's all there is; there isn't any more."

23. Complete the following quotation from Rudyard Kipling's "The Betrothed": "A woman is only a woman . . ."

24. "History is bunk" is a remark attributed to what man?

25. Fill in the missing word in this line by Will Rogers: "There is no more independence in ———— than there is in jail."

26. An unknown author wrote: "Ladies, to this advice give heed / In controlling men / If at first you don't succeed . . ." What is the remaining line?

Answers

1. "Diamond Lil."
2. Will Rogers.
3. "Here once the embattled farmers stood" (from Ralph Waldo Emerson's poem "Concord Hymn").
4. "Art for Art's Sake" (in Latin, "Ars Gratia Artis").
5. "Babbitt" (1922).
6. "Gentlemen Prefer Blondes."
7. Ernie Pyle.
8. Mark Twain.
9. James Whitcomb Riley.
10. He said it at the deathbed of Abraham Lincoln.
11. Will Rogers.
12. "Twelfth Night" (Act II, Scene 5).
13. "Pudd'nhead Wilson's Calendar."
14. "The Tempest" (Act I, Scene 1).
15. Will Rogers, in "The Illiterate Digest."
16. Henry Ford.

17. Greta Garbo.
18. Phineas T. Barnum.
19. Huey Long.
20. O. Henry.
21. O. Henry.
22. Ethel Barrymore, in "Sunday."
23. "But a good cigar is a smoke."
24. Henry Ford.
25. Politics.
26. "Why, cry, cry again."

GENERAL

1. After Lindbergh's flight to Paris in 1927, a female dentist's assistant from Lakeland, Fla., teamed up with pilot George Haldeman and set out to become the first woman transatlantic airplane rider, although she did not achieve her objective. Do you know her name?
2. What travel feat was achieved in 1911 by Galbraith P. Rodgers?
3. In 1894, Jacob S. Coxey led an "army" of 20,000 unemployed from the Midwest to what city?
4. In what city was the first Woolworth variety store opened?
5. John T. Scopes was convicted in 1925 of having taught evolution and he was fined. How much?
6. What were the Lancia, Franklin, Marmon, and Cleveland?
7. America is named for Amerigo Vespucci, who is believed to have made four voyages to the New World. The trips were made on behalf of what country?
8. Anna Jarvis of Philadelphia was very much responsible for an annual observance. Do you know which one?
9. Before construction began on the Empire State Building in 1930, what was on the site?
10. In early summer 1937, aviatrix Amelia Earhart Putnam disappeared while flying near Howland Island in the Pacific Ocean. Who else was lost on the flight?
11. What was the name of the dirigible that fell into a heavy sea off the New Jersey coast and broke up in April 1933?
12. Name the disastrous hurricane that swept up the East Coast of the U.S. in mid-October 1954 and caused more than 300 deaths.
13. To what accomplishment does the following account refer: "They just stared. Maybe they didn't hear me. Maybe I didn't hear them. Or maybe they thought I was just a crazy fool. An hour later I saw land"?
14. What airline used a four-engine flying boat named

"China Clipper" to introduce transpacific air service in 1935?

15. Where did the former French luxury liner "Normandie" burn and capsize in 1945?

16. In Greek mythology, what god dwelled on the highest peak of Mount Olympus?

17. What was the occupation of Joseph F. Crater?

18. What country is referred to as the "Roof of the World"?

19. In 1871, Henry Stanley located missing explorer David Livingstone. Where?

20. Do you know what Eugene Sandow's specialty was?

21. How did Johns Hopkins, founder of the university in Baltimore that bears his name, acquire his wealth?

22. What was the official price of gold before the dollar was devalued in 1934 and the value of gold raised to $35 per ounce?

23. Who issued "The Shadow Magazine" during the 1930s and '40s?

24. Name the publication that carried the headline "Wall Street Lays an Egg" in 1929.

25. A father and son directed construction of the Brooklyn Bridge, the largest suspension bridge in the world when it was completed in 1883. What were the names of these two engineers?

26. In the 1920s, 51-year-old millionaire Edward Browning married a 15-year-old girl named Frances Heenan. Their marriage and subsequent marital difficulties brought a nationwide spotlight on them. By what nicknames were they known?

27. Speeding the 188 miles from Memphis, Tenn., to Canton, Miss., on April 30, 1900, engineer Casey Jones was killed when his train crashed into a stalled freight. What was the name of his train?

28. What was the title of Britain's King Edward VIII before he became King in early 1936?

29. Who was known as "The Match King"?

30. Who were Solomon's parents?

31. What was the title of Billy Rose's newspaper column?

32. About how many cents per acre did Russia charge the United States for Alaska?

33. What street is usually thought of when the date October 29, 1929, is mentioned?

34. What is the name of the soft drink invented in Waco, Tex., in 1885 by a soda fountain clerk and perfected by chemist R. S. Lazenby?

35. How did Battle Creek, Mich., get its name?

36. For what in particular was Alvin (Shipwreck) Kelly known?

37. With what great inventor is Menlo Park, near East Orange, N.J., associated?

38. What was the name of the suit worn in the 1940s which consisted of a long jacket with heavily padded shoulders, wide lapels and cloth-covered buttons, and pants very wide at the knees, tapered to narrow cuffs?

39. Who was the first Secretary General of the United Nations and from what country was he?

40. What was the sculptured sundial at the New York World's Fair of 1939 called?

41. What was the name of the first child of English parents born in the Colony of Virginia? She was born on Roanoke Island in 1587.

42. Identify Lisa del Giocondo.

43. In what New Jersey community did Albert Einstein live?

44. Where in the U.S. was the flood that took 2,200 lives in 1889?

45. The man who was the first president of the U.S. Steel Corporation also founded Bethlehem Steel. His name?

46. In what community in France were the Duke of Windsor and Mrs. Wallis Warfield Simpson married?

47. John S. Pemberton, a pharmacist, developed a consumer product in 1886 that is a best seller today. What is it?

48. The area of the District of Columbia is 69 square miles. Do you know the original size of the District?

49. Name the doctor who delivered the Dionne quintuplets (May 28, 1934).

50. Ely Culbertson was an authority on what card game?

51. Sears, Roebuck, & Co. is named after Richard W. Sears and Alvah C. Roebuck. What were the occupations of Sears and Roebuck just before their mail-order business venture?

52. What was Mohandas K. Gandhi of India called?

53. Who gave a demonstration of the first liquid-fuel rocket, at Auburn, Mass., in 1926?

54. A fire at a Boston nightclub in 1942 caused 491 deaths and several hundred injuries. What was the name of the club?

55. For what have William W. and Andrew Smith been noted?

56. Miss Margaret Gorman of Washington, D.C., was the first winner of what contest?

57. A feature of the New York World's Fair of 1939 was a model city of the future. What was its name?

58. Who is believed to have built the Hanging Gardens of Babylon?

59. Albert, Otto, Alfred, Charles, and John were first names of well-known brothers. Who were they?

60. What was the official name of the exposition held in St. Louis in 1904?

61. "Whiz," "National," "Star-Spangled," "Sensation," and "Smash" were what kind of publications?

62. A mayor of New York City once read the funnies over the air during a newspaper strike, and afterward. Who was he?

63. What was the name of the mare ridden by Paul Revere on his midnight ride of April 18, 1775?

64. In 1956, an Italian luxury liner sank in the North Atlantic off Massachusetts after colliding with the Swedish liner "Stockholm." What was the name of the Italian ship?

65. Digging of the Panama Canal was started in 1882 by what country?

66. Cornelius Vanderbilt, Daniel Drew, Jay Gould, and James Fisk manipulated the stock of what railroad about a century ago?

67. Former Russian leader Leon Trotsky was killed in 1940. In what country was he living at the time?

68. For what magazine did the late Quentin Reynolds report during World War II?

69. Do you know at least one of the two states that never ratified the 18th (Prohibition) Amendment?

70. What was the name of the Boston nightclub that collapsed in July 1925, killing 44 people?

71. In an old legend, Pyramus and Thisbe were in love but tragedy intervened and both died before they could marry. In what ancient land are they supposed to have lived?

72. Can you name the blacksmith of the gods in either Roman or Greek mythology?

73. What is the American card game based on the French bezique and the German sixty-six?

74. In what city was the Ringling Brothers and Barnum & Bailey Circus fire in 1944?

75. Pandora opened a box and released all of man's troubles. Who gave the box to her?

76. What concert pianist was also a prime minister of Poland?

77. What kind of vehicle had a "drop frame" model?

78. Name the airplane manufacturer that made the Condor.

79. Who set a transcontinental airplane speed record by flying from Los Angeles to New York in 7 hours and 28 minutes in 1937?

80. Pan American World Airways began regular transatlantic passenger flights in mid-1939, between New York and Lisbon, Portugal. What was the name of the flying boat that started the service?

81. The burning of the "Morro Castle" caused 134 lives to be lost in 1934. What was the "Morro Castle"?

82. When using a regular deck of 52 cards for playing the game of Old Maid, which card is used for the Old Maid?

83. What begins: "I swear by Apollo Physician, by Asclepius, by Health, by Panacea, and by all the gods and goddesses, making them my witnesses, that I will carry out . . ."

84. For what is William Holmes McGuffey remembered?

85. An office building completed in New York in 1913 was then the tallest building in the world. Name it.

86. In mythology, Sif was the wife of what god?

87. Matador, the block game, and muggins are all forms of what game?

88. How did the "Lusitania" sink?

89. Charles A. Lindbergh was a captain when he flew to Paris on May 20–21, 1927. What was his rank when he was welcomed by President Coolidge in Washington on June 11?

90. What company owned the "Titanic"?

91. In the early 1930s, the Townsend Plan was a proposal for a national pension for persons 60 years and older. How much per month?

92. Douglas Corrigan flew the wrong way and landed in Dublin, Ireland, in 1938. From where did he take off?

93. Give the full name of the writer known as F.P.A.

94. A chemist who worked for what company was granted a patent on nylon in the late 1930s?

95. What was the color of the eagle which was the symbol of the National Recovery Administration?

96. At the beginning of the card game of "clock," the deck of 52 cards is dealt into how many packets or piles?

97. Name either the airfield from which Charles Lindbergh took off or the one on which he landed in his famous New York-to-Paris flight in 1927.

98. "Civilization is on trial" was a comment by the defense attorney in the 1925 John Scopes evolution trial. Name the attorney.

99. Negro spiritual leader George Baker was better known by what name?

100. The Columbian Exposition in Chicago during the 1890s commemorated what?

101. What was the last food item still to be rationed after World War II ended?

102. The Perisphere and 700-foot-high Trylon were symbols of what fair?

103. In mythology, what happened to Thor's hammer after he threw it?

104. The Virgin Islands were purchased by the U.S. in 1931 from what country?

105. The amendment to the Constitution granting suffrage for women went into effect about two months before what national election?

106. In what city did the Great Atlantic & Pacific Tea Company start? What is the company usually called?

107. Jackson, Miss., Jefferson City, Mo., and Madison, Wis., are state capitals named for U.S. Presidents. There is one other. Do you know it?

108. San Francisco suffered a severe earthquake and fire in 1906. In what large city was there a big fire two years earlier?

109. Give the family name of the German Kaiser Wilhelm.

110. "The Birds of America," published in the 19th century, contains numerous sketches made by what well-known American?

111. Within ten years, when were electric lights first used on Broadway in New York City?

112. An epidemic of what disease caused more than half a million Americans to die in 1918?

113. What was the first passenger railroad in the United States?

114. Identify the historic personality who is said to have learned a lesson in persistency from watching a spider.

115. Name the railroad that operated the "M-10,000," which began running in February 1934.

116. Name the explorer, employed by the Dutch East India Company, who sailed the sloop "Half Moon" into what are now New York Harbor and Albany, in 1609.

117. What kind of flowers are depicted in one of the best-known paintings by Van Gogh?

118. Who headed the party of explorers that traveled by air from Little America in the Antarctic to the South Pole and back, in 1929?

119. Who was the woman passenger who accompanied Wilmer Stultz on his flight from Newfoundland to Wales in 1928, becoming the first woman to fly the Atlantic?

120. Within four knots, what was the speed of the "Titanic" when a lookout spotted the fateful iceberg?

121. Transcontinental service for what form of travel was introduced by Pickwick Stages in 1928?

122. Who was the famous father of daughters Marjorie, Natalie, Edna, Marilyn, and Janet?

123. Name the chief of the Soviet secret police who was dismissed in mid-1953, called an enemy of the people, and executed before the end of the year.

124. A card game known as "Sevens" or "Parliament" is generally known by what name?

125. The U.S. frigate "Constitution" ("Old Ironsides") was launched at Boston in September 1797. What frigate was launched at Baltimore two weeks earlier?

126. Long fingernails became a fad in the early 1930s. Name the personality who supposedly introduced them.

127. An old card game called "the Farm" has two other names today. What are they?

128. Jay Gould and William H. Vanderbilt consolidated Western Union, American Union, and the Atlantic and Pacific companies into what single company, in 1881?

129. Nancy Green worked at the Chicago World's Fair of

1893 where she cooked pancakes, sang, and told stories of the old South. She worked for the R. T. Davis Milling Company. By what name was she known?

130. The first electric street railway in the U.S. started operations in 1885, in what city?

131. In 1912, an act of Congress set a limit on the number of hours federal employees were to work in a regular day. How many?

132. Who was the self-appointed head of "The House of Prayer for All People"? He died in 1960 and left an estate of several million dollars.

133. Before the card game Five Hundred came along in the early 1900s, what was considered the most popular card game in the U.S.?

134. Today, TWA stands for Trans-World Airlines. What did the letters represent when they were adopted in 1930?

135. The Pony Express, a mail service between St. Joseph, Mo., and San Francisco, was established in 1860 and ended in what year (within four)?

136. Name a magazine that mentioned the reading time needed for articles.

137. Where in the United States was the peace treaty between Russia and Japan signed, in 1905?

Answers

1. Ruth Elder.
2. He made the first coast-to-coast flight in the U.S., from New York City to Pasadena, taking 49 days.
3. Washington, D.C.
4. Utica, N.Y. (1879).
5. $100 and costs. On appeal, the fine was reversed on a technicality.
6. Early automobiles.
7. Spain, although Vespucci was an Italian.
8. Mother's Day.
9. The old Waldorf-Astoria Hotel.
10. Copilot and navigator Fred Noonan.
11. "Akron" (74 deaths).
12. Hazel.
13. It is part of Charles A. Lindbergh's story of his nonstop flight to Paris.
14. Pan American Airways.
15. At a pier in New York City.
16. Zeus, who controlled the sky and ruled the gods. (In Roman mythology, Zeus is known as Jupiter.)

17. Justice of the New York State Supreme Court. He disappeared in August 1930 and has never been found.
18. Tibet.
19. Ujiji, on Lake Tanganyika in eastern Africa.
20. Weight lifting.
21. Principally from the wholesale grocery business.
22. $20.67 per ounce.
23. Street and Smith.
24. "Variety."
25. John Augustus and Washington Augustus Roebling.
26. "Daddy" and "Peaches."
27. Illinois Central's "Cannonball Express."
28. Prince of Wales.
29. Ivar Kreuger.
30. David and Bathsheba.
31. "Pitching Horseshoes."
32. Two. The price was $7.2 million in 1867.
33. Wall Street, New York City. The stock market crashed that day.
34. Dr Pepper.
35. From an 1824 battle between a surveying party and Indians.
36. Flagpole sitting.
37. Thomas A. Edison.
38. Zoot suit. Accessories were wide-brimmed hats, long key chains, and wide, flowered ties.
39. Trygve Lie; Norway.
40. "Time and the Fate of Man."
41. Virginia Dare.
42. Her portrait by Leonardo da Vinci is the famous "Mona Lisa."
43. Princeton.
44. Johnstown, Pa.
45. Charles M. Schwab.
46. Monts.
47. Coca-Cola.
48. 100 square miles (10 miles square). Land south of the Potomac was returned to Virginia.
49. Dr. Allan R. Dafoe.
50. Bridge.
51. Sears was a railroad station agent; Roebuck, a watchmaker.
52. "Mahatma" ("Great Soul").
53. Dr. Robert H. Goddard.
54. Cocoanut Grove.
55. Cough drops. William is "Trade" and Andrew, "Mark."
56. Miss America (1921).
57. Democracity.
58. Nebuchadnezzar.
59. The Ringling Brothers, of circus renown.
60. Louisiana Purchase Exposition.
61. Comic books.
62. Fiorello La Guardia.
63. Brown Beauty.
64. "Andrea Doria."

65. France.
66. Erie Railroad.
67. Mexico.
68. "Collier's."
69. Connecticut and Rhode Island.
70. Pickwick Club.
71. Babylon.
72. Vulcan (Roman); Hephaestus (Greek).
73. Pinochle.
74. Hartford, Conn.
75. Zeus.
76. Ignace Paderewski.
77. Bicycle.
78. Curtiss.
79. Howard Hughes.
80. Dixie Clipper.
81. A cruise liner. It burned off Asbury Park, N.J.
82. Any one of the four queens. It is designated before the game begins.
83. The Physician's (Hippocratic) Oath. This is a translation from Latin.
84. McGuffey's Readers, standard elementary-school textbooks for a long time.
85. Woolworth Building (60 floors).
86. Thor.
87. Dominoes.
88. It was hit by a German submarine's torpedo in 1915.
89. Colonel.
90. White Star Lines.
91. $200.
92. Floyd Bennett Field, Brooklyn, N.Y.
93. Franklin Pierce Adams.
94. Du Pont. The chemist was Wallace Hume Carothers.
95. Blue.
96. 13 (four cards each).
97. He left from Roosevelt Field, Long Island, and landed at Le Bourget in Paris.
98. Clarence Darrow.
99. Father Divine.
100. The 400th anniversary of the discovery of America.
101. Sugar.
102. New York World's Fair (1939–40).
103. It returned to his hand.
104. Denmark. They had been known as the Danish West Indies.
105. 1920. Warren G. Harding was elected.
106. New York (1859). The A&P.
107. Lincoln, Nebr.
108. Baltimore.
109. Hohenzollern.
110. John James Audubon.
111. 1880.
112. Influenza.
113. Baltimore and Ohio, which began operating in 1830.

114. Robert the Bruce, a Scotch hero.
115. Union Pacific.
116. Henry Hudson.
117. Sunflowers.
118. Commander Richard E. Byrd.
119. Amelia Earhart.
120. 22 ½ knots.
121. Bus.
122. Eddie Cantor.
123. Lavrenti P. Beria.
124. Fan-tan.
125. "Constellation."
126. Marlene Dietrich.
127. "Black Jack"; Twenty-one."
128. Western Union Telegraph Company.
129. "Aunt Jemima," whose real-life characterization she did for many years.
130. Baltimore.
131. Eight.
132. Charles Manuel ("Sweet Daddy") Grace.
133. Euchre.
134. Transcontinental and Western Air.
135. 1861. The opening of the transcontinental telegraph made the Pony Express unnecessary.
136. "Liberty."
137. Portsmouth, N.H. (at the U.S. Navy Yard).

Index to Persons